The Adventures of
DAYNE TRAVELER
REFLECTIONS
VOLUME 2

DANIEL POPE WITH DAVID GRAY

FOLGER ROSS PUBLICATIONS

Swathmore, PA

The Adventures of Dayne Traveler: Reflections   Volume 2

© 2011 by Daniel Pope with David Gray
All Rights Reserved

For more inquiries on Dayne Traveler's adventures and work, visit us at:
WWW.DAYNETRAVELER.COM

Join us on Facebook: DAYNE TRAVELER

ISBN: 978-0-9771462-3-9

Printed in the United States of America

THIS BOOK IS DEDICATED TO MY DAUGHTER, RACHAEL-
GOD'S SWEETEST GIFT TO ME.

CONTENTS

INTRODUCTION

I first encountered Daniel Pope about twenty years ago at church. I didn't like him. "Too over-the-top," I told myself. "Somebody ought to knock him off his high horse." Daniel was supposed to be some kind of martial arts champion. He was supposed to be really good. My problem was that I had earned my black belt in a different school, and "n'ere the twain shall meet." It's a guy thing.

But there was a grudging sort of mutual respect between us. Confidence has a way of expressing itself in a person's posture, his gaze, his walk; in his air. A visitor to the church observing us might have wondered just which one of us actually owned the building. We were both convinced of our individual abilities and we recognized each other's self-confidence. But since neither one of us is of a nature to back down, it was an unspoken respect. Like I said, it's a guy thing. Our attitudes would evolve.

One Sunday morning we found ourselves in the same Sunday school class. Daniel made some interesting points in the discussions and I thought, "Hmmm, there might be more to this guy than I realized!" Little did I suspect that he was thinking the same thing about me. Can you believe it; we came to like each other! A friendship developed, and eventually the subject of martial arts was no longer taboo.

I am twenty years older than Daniel, and have been able to maintain my fitness through hard work, but I wasn't getting any regular exercise. He said to me, "David, you ought to get back into training." So I did. He learned a lot about me as a student, and I learned even more about him as an instructor, and as an actual karate champion. In truth, I learned more in four hours of his instruction than in two years of my other training. Fine points. Technical points. Strategies. "Why has no one ever told me these things," I wondered. Then I figured it out – they didn't know these things. It takes years and years of experience and thousands of matches to learn what Daniel teaches.

Daniel knew that I had written some poetry and was finishing a novel, so one day he handed me a number of pages saying, "You know, I'm doing some writing too! Could you look it over?" I did, and so began my partnership with him as the editor of his first book with Lorraine Ranalli, *The Adventures of Dayne Traveler.* It was here that I was introduced to Daniel's fascinating alter-ego. It was an interesting journey for me, but not as fascinating as Dayne Traveler's adventures. And now I've been asked to co-write the sequel.

At first, trying to evaluate or even understand Dayne seems a daunting task. Why is he that way? After long observation, however, a reasonable explanation emerges. It's the same passionate energy that drove his successful karate career that fuels Daniel's zest for life. The commonplace just doesn't hack it. Life must be experienced at its limits, and the alleged boundaries are there to be discovered and tested. Why eat ice cream when you can have a sundae? Why have a sundae without whipped cream and a cherry. And while we're at it, how about some wet nuts and sprinkles! And would you super-size that order please?!

The point of Dayne Traveler's adventures isn't a mere hedonistic pursuit of pleasure. It's a thorough investigation of interesting and exciting activities. It's an opportunity to experience and to explore, with an insatiable appetite to learn, so that the joy of the discovery can be shared with others who may not have the opportunity, or the nerve, to test the waters themselves.

That "high horse" provides a grand view of life's fascinating facets. To some, it seems an affront. On closer inspection, though, it's simply an expression of Daniel's joy of life, revealing a childlike sense of fun and a love of humanity. You may want to knock him off his horse. He wants to pull you up for a better look.

— David Gray
Writer and Editor

FORWARD: A LOOK INSIDE

In my previous book I interviewed Daniel Pope. I felt it was the polite thing to do since Mr. Pope's martial arts career has funded most of my adventures. Now Daniel has asked to interview me. "Turnabout's fair play," he told me. Personally, I think he just wanted to appear in another of my books. Whatever the reason might be, I decided to humor him and agreed to be interviewed. I was eager to see what might be of interest to my readers, and to discover what it was that curious minds wanted to know. The following is a series of questions from the readers.

Daniel P: *Dayne, here's a question for you. It reads, "You travel all over, searching for excitement. Doesn't it wear you down sometimes? Don't you get a bit tired of it? Why do you do it?"*

Dayne T: Tired of it? Are you kidding? That's like asking me if I get tired of breathing! I live for it! It's what keeps me going. But why do I do it? I guess that goes back to my grandfather. Now he was a world traveler! On Friday nights after dinner the family would gather around the kitchen table and he'd put on a slide show using the fridge as a screen. I was fascinated by it. It was fun to see where Pop had recently been, riding on a camel, or swimming in Hawaii. He proudly wore a jacket with patches all over it showing all the places he had traveled. Poppy was a hard-working man – he owned a deli and worked 12 to 15 hour days, but he always made time for travel and play. He told me, "Dayne, travel every chance you get. No college education can match it!" Then years later when I traveled, I was able to come home and tell him where I'd been and show him pictures of my adventures. I hope I gave him as much joy as he gave me.

DP: *"As much fun as it all sounds, it seems that there's always something going wrong," one reader says. "I think I'd be a little nervous traveling with you. I've even heard that some of your friends choose to pass on your invitations to join in. What do you say to them?"*

DT: My Aunt Karen once remarked, "I'm surprised that you can get anybody to go along with you anymore!" I understood her trepidation. She was probably thinking of the time I was caught in a stampeding herd of buffalo in a rented Subaru. Or when I unexpectedly found myself being chased by a 1200-pound moose. Or six feet from a bear in my path. Or when I jumped off a motorcycle to avoid an even worse fate. Sometimes things just happen when I'm around. Even I don't understand it, but I'm used to it. Some people say I've got a death-wish, but that's not right – I've got a life-wish. I don't deliberately create dangerous situations, but I have to admit, I feel most alive while it's happening.

I invite others to come along and share some of the experiences. I want them to step out of their comfort zone and expand their horizons. It might not be for everyone, but there are some who just never had the opportunity, or maybe they couldn't afford it. Or maybe they just don't know where to find the adventure. I think there's a little bit of Dayne Traveler in everybody just waiting to get out, and I'm happy to be a bridge to their adventures. I've been privileged to be able to guide many groups to discovering just how far they can go. But it's never my intention to put them at risk.

DP: *One of your readers wanted me to ask you this question – "How do you decide what your next* *adventure will be?"*

DT: Even I don't know what's around the next bend. Adventures might depend on the time of the year, or something I'm interested in at the time, but if an opportunity arises, I pounce on it.

DP: *In all of your travels, do you have any regrets?*

DT: Not really, except maybe not being able to stay longer at some destination I've enjoyed.

DP: *Another reader asks how you relax and wants to know if you get any downtime?*

DT: Believe it or not, I go to great lengths to have downtime and unwind. I like taking walks and leisurely bike rides. I might relax with a book in my log cabin in the Poconos. I love watching sports. But my batteries get recharged by doing my morning devotions and reading my Bible. Without a rejuvenated spirit, I couldn't do all the things I enjoy.

DP: *Living the way you do, you'd better stay close to God! Here's another question. "Don't take offense," she says. "After reading your exploits, some people might think that you live outside of the realm of normal human experience. Are you even in touch with the normal world; with everyday people?"*

DT: No offence is taken. I know "normal" people and human nature all too well, but I also understand the need for both discipline and pleasure. If all you know about me is the exploits, the question makes sense but, as I've said before, you have to work hard if you want to play hard. I want to live a full and productive life, and that starts with having a relationship with Jesus to keep it in balance.

DP: *Here's an interesting question. "If you could take anybody you wanted to lunch, past or present, who would it be?"*

DT: It goes without saying that in the "past" category, it would be Jesus Christ, but I feel a little strange saying I'd take the Lord to lunch. It sounds disrespectful. I'll change my answer to King David, or maybe his son, Solomon. I've got a few questions for them, believe me.

DP: *Athletes have medals and trophies, writers get literary awards for their efforts, and all sorts of professionals receive recognition - signs of their personal success. What do you have?*

D T: Pictures! Thank God for photo albums! If my home was burning,after getting my family to safety, I'd run back in and grab the photo albums.

DP: *Seriously now, what would you say was the most thrilling of all your adventures?*

DT: That's got to be the most frequently asked question of all. And my answer is always the same. I can't single out any one adventure over another. They've all been meaningful, educational and rewarding, and I've appreciated each one. They're all spectacular in their own ways and I can't rank them.

DP: *What would be your most disastrous adventure? Does any one of them stand out?*

DT: You know, that's the second most frequently asked question! Yes, one stands out. Without question, it was my death-defying kayaking experience. I did a foolish thing, going out alone in dangerous circumstances, and it didn't go well. In my first book the episode may have been treated a little lightheartedly, but it was really a close call. I had literally seconds to live, and really thought it would be the end of my story!

DP: *Here's a final question for you. If you knew that you only had one more adventure in you, what would it be? Is there one special thing you have yet to do? Would you do something new, or would you try to repeat an adventure you've already had?*

DT: I dearly love all the adventures, and I love repeats too, but it would be something new. I've always believed that the greatest adventure is yet to happen. Don't misunderstand – I don't want to leave here prematurely, but the adventure I look most forward to is exploring heaven, the place that God's prepared for us.

◊   JOHN 14:2-3 *In my Father's house are many rooms; if it were not so, I would have told you. I am going there to prepare a place for you. And if I go and prepare a place for you, I will come back and take you to be with me, that you may also be where I am.*

"It is not the critic who counts, not the man who points out how the strong man stumbles, or where the doer of deeds could have done them better. The credit belongs to the man in the arena, whose face is marred by dust and sweat and blood, who strives valiantly... who knows the great devotions, who spends himself in a worthy cause, who at the best knows in the end the triumph of high achievement, and who at the worst, if he fails, at least fails while daring greatly, so that his place shall never be with those cold and timid souls who have never known neither victory nor defeat."

— Teddy Roosevelt

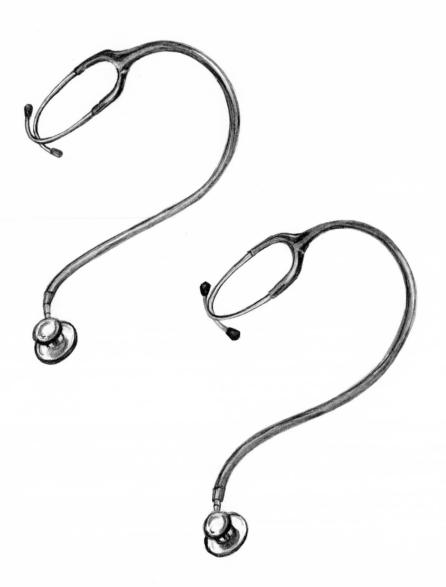

Not Again!

I was relaxing in the Poconos when the phone call came, pretty sure it would be good news. After all, I'd been through it before. This time I had all the bases covered. There was no logical reason to expect a bad report. I felt pretty good – cautiously optimistic, as they say. My successful sport karate career was winding down and I was looking forward to my next adventure. I had time now to relax; time to enjoy my family and friends, and these peaceful retreats to the log cabin. Life was good. When the phone rang, caller ID indicated it was my doctor.

"Hi, Dr. Roush, how are you doing?"

"I'm fine, I guess," he answered. "The results came back. I don't know any easy way to say this. The biopsy tested positive: Non-Hodgkin's lymphoma. It's returned."

There was a moment of silence. He continued,

"Are you OK?"

"Yes," I answered, "I'm OK. So what's next? Where do we go from here?"

"Come in on Monday, say nine o'clock, and we'll go over your options."

"OK, Doctor, I'll see you Monday. Thanks for getting back to me so quickly. Goodbye."

In just thirty seconds my world had been turned upside down. Again. Yet again! "How can this be happening?" I asked out loud. This was a hard one to accept. It was just about three years ago when they cut a cancerous lymph node out of my thigh.

I had my twenty radiation treatments. I did everything they told me to do, keeping careful watch over my health. I took my vitamin supplements. I worked out regularly and always knew what I weighed. I knew my blood pressure and heart rate. I got the proper amount of sleep. I ate wisely. I hydrated. Every six-month checkup was fine. And the last one was just a few months ago.

"How can this be happening again," I repeated.

A few weeks earlier, I had felt a lump under the skin near my elbow. I knew immediately what it was. It was just like the one I had on my thigh.

"Maybe you should have Dr. Roush look at it," I was told. I remained calm, not wanting to frighten anyone.

"It's a swollen lymph gland," my doctor told me, but just because it's swollen, that doesn't mean the cancer's returned. We'll remove it and send it out for a biopsy just to make sure. Don't lose too much sleep over this." I had been so confident that the cancer in my thigh had been a one-time thing. Would I now have to be looking over my shoulder for the rest of my life?

So there I was, staring out the log cabin window in a state of confusion, facing my own mortality – again. I needed to gather myself and call my family. They needed me to be strong.

Some people get mad at God when life doesn't go their way, but being angry at the Almighty was the furthest thing from my mind. I fell to my knees. "Lord, I love you." I said out loud. "You've blessed me with more than I ever could have imagined or deserved. I trusted you the last time and I'll trust you again. No matter what happens, my faith is in you." Slowly, my confusion dissipated. My strength was restored. I was at peace. Once again I found myself reminiscing and relishing the memories of all the wonderful experiences I had been given, and all the interesting people I've been blessed to know.

◊ PSALM 27:1 *The Lord is my light and my salvation – whom then shall I fear?*

WHISTLING IN THE DARK

Looking straight down the snow-covered crack in the mountain brought up every fear-of-heights/anxiety-bordering-on-panic/no-way-out/fight-or-flight memory in my mind. My legs felt like lead. The icy wind was sucking the breath from my lungs. "Inhale," I told myself. "Clear your mind! You can do this. You've been trained by the best." But there was another voice in my head saying, "What in the world are you doing? Are you nuts? Just turn around and go home. No one would blame you? Who would even know?" Of course, the answer to that last one is, "I would!"

I love to ski! Over the years my skill has improved and I've taken on some challenges that I would never have dreamed of at the start. I read the ski magazines with interest, especially when they give their annual ranking of the best slopes in North America. Year after year, at the top of the lists, I'd fine Whistler-Blackcomb in British Columbia. Among nature's beauties I especially like waterfalls and couloirs (pronounced KOO-lar – those steep vertical gorges in the face of mountains.) I can't ski down a waterfall, but a couloir? Now that was something I had to try! I decided to find out what all the Whistler hype was about. I wanted to see for myself what was said to be among the best in the world. Now it was here right in front of me and there was no doubt in my mind – This really was one of the best. Surrounding me were some of the wildest and most difficult slopes I had ever seen.

When you travel to ski locations anywhere in the world

you find a universal code indicating the difficulty of the slopes. A slope marked with a circle is for beginners. A square indicates "intermediate." But the black diamond says "this is the most difficult slope that the mountain has to offer." That's where I like to hang out. That's where you'll find me! That's not to say that all black diamonds are equal. Just that it's the hardest slope on that mountain. A black diamond in the east might only be an intermediate slope out west. But the slopes I had my eye on at Whistler-Blackcomb were for experts only - double-black diamonds! Couloirs! This was serious stuff. Very serious stuff. And I wanted to see if I had the skill to play with the big boys.

If I've learned anything, it's that it pays to be taught by professionals. I found this to be true in sports, music and even in hobbies like horseback riding. But I didn't always heed my own advice. I had to learn the hard way. For instance, after I enthusiastically strapped on my first pair of skis, I tore up more packed powder with my rear end than with my new skis because I had taken my athletic ability for granted. It wasn't my athleticism that steered me down the mountain, but my sore derriere, and it prompted me to visit the ski lodge in search of lessons. I discovered that I needed to approach skiing just as I had every other endeavor in my life. I needed instruction. After an instructor had established the fundamentals, my ski experience became much more enjoyable. And I found that articles I read on skiing made more sense too, which re-enforced what I had been taught. This confirmed my theory on learning: books and videos are great tools, but there is no substitute for professional instruction.

Another hard lesson was that your proficiency in an endeavor doesn't necessarily qualify you as an instructor. The first time I took my daughter to ski, I was feeling really confident. She was just eight years old then and I had the best intentions to teach her everything I knew. What a catastrophe! Although I had coached her successfully in other sports, I simply did not have the necessary knowledge to teach her to ski. During that one outing I must have set a record for falling. In a few hours of trying to teach my daughter, I ate more snow than I had while skiing alone the whole year. This miserable experience nearly turned my daughter off skiing for good. My ski instructor at Jackson Hole legitimized my frustrations.

"Teaching a family member to ski never works," he told me. "I've seen some of the biggest arguments occur when a boyfriend and girlfriend, or a husband and wife try to teach each other how to ski. The sad part is that the one being taught has such a negative experience that sometimes they never return. Good instructors are made, not born."

That's what nearly happened on another occasion when I took another family member skiing. Yep, I hadn't learned the lesson with my daughter. The dynamics between us were so explosive that they could have triggered an avalanche. We attracted a small audience as she stubbornly, but justifiably, took her skis off and stood indignantly on top of the mountain until I summoned the ski patrol. I was thoroughly embarrassed. Back at the lodge, she joyfully exclaimed that she had more fun on the snowmobile ride down the mountain than she had had the entire day trying to learn to ski from me. Fortunately, I was able to salvage the situation by getting some lessons for her. Learning from an objective professional who is accustomed to training skiers at all levels makes a world of difference.

I planned a week of skiing at Whistler-Blackcomb, the two mountains that make up this legendary skiers' paradise. Would a week be enough time? Not only is it a large resort, but Whistler has the highest elevation in North America, a 5280 foot rise from the base to the summit. There are more than a hundred different runs in its seven-thousand acres with steeps that will blow your mind, and on one of those runs you can ski non-stop for an amazing seven miles. Whistler-Blackcomb also boasts one of the longest ski seasons to be found, from November into June. This place is world-class. But most alluring to me were the many couloirs just waiting to be sampled!

I knew that I wasn't ready for a couloir yet. They're the sort of thing that can get you killed. They reminded me of a commercial I had seen where a crazy man on a snowboard is dropped from a helicopter onto the peak of a mountain, and he proceeds to board – straight down. What I needed was a qualified instructor, and luck was with me. A chance cancellation by one skier enabled me to contract one of the best instructors at Whistler, an amazing 5 ft 6 inch Romanian dynamo. He was extremely athletic and skilled. I asked him if it was possible for him to teach me to ski a couloir by the end of the week. After considering my previous experience, he concluded,

"Yes, I can teach you. If you learn the techniques, and practice my drills – if you follow all the steps and apply yourself seriously, we can do it."

That week with him was like cramming for an exam. But I was determined to succeed. I stayed alert. I drilled. I practiced. I visualized. I was ready! Or so I thought. The day of testing arrived all too soon.

The ski lift to Harmony Hut at the summit of Whistler offered spectacular views of the mountain, and near the top my instructor pointed out the couloirs to our left on Harmony Ridge.

"That's where we're headed," he said.

"Hmmmm," I thought, "That doesn't look so bad from here!"

There weren't many skiers on the lift. Most had gotten off farther below. Now at the top, four others went to the right to the advanced bowls and runs. Only my instructor and I turned to the left. The snow packed path curved around the ridge, hugging the rock wall of the mountain. As we traversed, the path got narrower and narrower and then, unexpectedly, ended. Four feet to the left was the cliff I was expected to jump off. The steepness of the slope – you couldn't even call it a slope – and the vast expanse of air before us made my mind spin. I thought I felt myself falling forward, and grabbed onto the rock wall with a gasp while my instructor skied nonchalantly toward the edge, spun 180 degrees, and stopped with the back of his skis hanging over the edge.

"All right, Dayne, this is it! This is what we prepared for all week. You have the skills you need. All you have to do now is put them to work and believe in yourself."

"Give me a minute," I said, still grasping the wall. I felt slightly sick, unable even to look down the sheer drop. It didn't seem humanly possible to ski down this terrain. There was no room for error. One mistake and I'd be falling for a long, long time. I could picture a tumble. I could envision my own personal avalanche. No! Wrong image! Wrong image! Thirty seconds of silence passed. I had to get myself together. He was being very patient with me, but I could tell that he was getting frustrated.

"Remember your lessons, Dayne. Do as we practiced. Were all the drills for nothing?" he demanded. "Come to the edge." I couldn't move. "Look, Dayne, it's time. Either do it now or take off your skis and go back!"

That worked. I knew what I had to do. I understand drills and instruction. I know about muscle memory and conditioned responses. I appreciate how good training enables you to react in the appropriate manner despite fear or stress. In my brain I knew I had the skills from the lessons, but this was really, really intense. My mental struggle was apparent.

"OK, Dayne," he said firmly, "try this. Rather than dropping straight in, sit down and work your way to the side of the chute so you can traverse your way in. Once you're in, don't hug the mountain," he warned. "Keep your chest pointing downhill and your weight forward. Do what you've been taught!"

I'd never forgive myself if I backed out now. It would be a real test for me but I figured that this alternative method of entry was better than the standard death leap from the edge. After a short but intense prayer, I traversed in, did a pole check, and then, right on cue, all of the training took over. There I was, dropping at nearly a free fall, skiing a couloir in one of the best locations in the world! It was exhilarating! Incredible! Can I say it, fun! After about a dozen turns I wanted to take it all in. Picture going over a waterfall and, midway, stopping to look around at the scenery. That's what it was like. Time seemed to stand still. Imagine the incredible panorama of some of the most beautiful landscapes in North America. It was a sight that very few people get to see. It was a blessed moment. And it was my own personal Super Bowl!

◊   PSALM 34:4-5 *I sought the Lord and he answered me; he delivered me from all my fears. Those who look to him are radiant; their faces are never covered with shame.*

LET'S BE FRIENDS

My life has been full of zany twists and turns, some coming when least expected, but I wouldn't have it any other way. Looking back on some of my adventures, though, I'm amazed that I haven't gotten into more serious jams than I have. With my spontaneous nature, I've learned that I need to depend on the good counsel of others. I wish that, when I was younger, I had been willing to listen to such advice: Recently, as I was reading in the book of Proverbs, an occurrence from my youth crossed my mind. It was a revelation for me to see how much I've grown. This story could have had a bad ending, but it turned out to be a good lesson instead.

I was in my early twenties, and had only recently begun my career. Understand that the martial arts present double-edged possibilities. Ideally, the result should be a healthy balance of self discipline, physical strength and a respect and appreciation for others. An egotistical and immature personality, however, can slip over to the dark side if care is not taken. At times, I was such a person.

I was a successful sport karate champion, but friction had developed between a fellow martial artist and me. My friends were a little too vocal about my accomplishments, and had apparently made some rash statements about what the result of our squaring off would be. Of course, his friends countered with similar statements, and so began an escalation of animosity and intrigue. The funny thing was that we had never even met! All of the information either of us had ever received was secondhand, causing both of us to be swayed by emotional statements. The next competition was a long way off, so rather than waiting, he telephoned me, emotionally berated me, questioned my manhood, and described what he would do to me when we finally met.

"We don't have to wait for the next tournament," I snapped back angrily, "Let's do it now!" It was a foolish thing to say, but that's what pride can do in an immature mind. It was the required response to a challenge. We agreed to meet in an hour at a neutral location – a local parking lot at high noon.

I showed up ahead of time. True to my competitive nature, I wanted to warm up before the showdown. To my amazement, my angry foe arrived in a long, tinted-glass limousine. I began to have second thoughts. I couldn't see if he had a posse with him. It's not that I lacked confidence, because at this time I was entering my absolute prime. I was six feet tall, 144 pounds, and had only 5% body fat. But out of the limo emerged a five foot nine, 220 pound machine, cut like Waterford crystal. I had only ever seen him from a distance, but now he was coming straight toward me at a fast pace, looking larger and larger. They say "discretion is the better part of valor."

"You sure you don't want to talk about this?" I asked. (I wanted to be fair.)

"Not a chance," he said angrily, putting up his hands. "We're gonna get it on right now."

And so the exchange of blows began. I gave as good as I took, and took as good as I gave. The scuffle moved into the street, and eventually we ended up on the ground wrestling. Our clothes were getting torn and there was blood coming from various places. It wasn't pretty. I was in a position of advantage and was just about to give him a good stiff right, when suddenly, I looked up and there was a police car. One of the local businessmen had dropped the dime.

I take pride in being able to think fast on my feet. This instance was no exception – I just hoped that my opponent would be quick enough to follow my lead and go along with me, before we were both taken for a ride that we didn't want to take.

"What do you think you're doing?" the cop demanded.

"Aw, every time I see this guy we start rough housing," I said as we stood and dusted ourselves off. "We couldn't wait for the upcoming tournament." To my surprise, my adversary smilingly went along with me.

"Yeah, Dayne always thinks that he's the best," he smiled, gently punching my shoulder. The cop gave us a doubtful look.

"You guys always mess around like this, with bloody mouths and your shirts torn off your backs?"

"Aw, this is nothin'," I told him, wrapping my arm around my new pal. "You should have seen us last week." Then he wrapped his muscular arm around me like a good buddy.

"Yeah, now that was fun!" he said.

"So nobody's going to press charges?"

"Heck, no, what for?" I asked. We both apologized to the officer for the misunderstanding, hoping to get off without a hassle. It almost worked.

"Look, guys," he told us, "you can't be doing this sort of thing." We held our breath. "You're going to get a $100 fine for disturbing the peace." After doing his job, he told us, "Now get out of here, and don't let me see any more of this or you'll really have to pay."

My newfound buddy invited me into his limo. "Have a nice day,' he said cheerfully to the policeman.

"Take care, officer," I added, as he drove off.

To my relief, there were no others inside in the limo. We

were alone. We both had a good laugh. Our issues got sorted out and we realized just how foolish we had been. So the air was cleared, and at the expense of a few bruises and $100, I had made a new friend.

A few weeks later, he picked me up in the same limousine and took me to a Phillies game. We never did match up in competition.

◊   PROV 13:17   *A quick-tempered man does foolish things...*

◊   PROV 15:1   *A gentle answer turns away wrath, but a harsh word stirs up anger.*

◊   PROV 16:32   *Better a patient man than a warrior; a man who controls his temper than one who takes a city.*

◊   PROV 17:19   *He who loves a quarrel loves sin...*

◊   PROV 17:28   *Even a fool is thought wise if he keeps silent, and discerning if he holds his tongue.*

◊   PROV 18:6   *A fool's lips bring him strife, and his mouth invites a beating.*

BEAR TALES

There is no way around it and no other way to say it; I find pure exhilaration when hiking in the woods where bears live. Maybe it's my sense of adventure. Maybe, like some people, I just need something more. I feel alive knowing I'm not the biggest, baddest creature in the woods. An average male black bear can grow up to 7 ft long and can weigh over 500 pounds. Compared to my 6 ft and 170 pounds, the black bear is far more dangerous than I am, and that gives the adventure an edge

The Keystone State can boast that they have one of the healthiest black bear populations in North America, but it wasn't always so. In the 1970's, Pennsylvania's bear population had shrunk to three or four thousand. Now the bear population has had an unprecedented recovery with over 14,000 black bears. Every March, researchers visit bear dens before the bears emerged from hibernation. Biologists collar them to electronically gather information so they can track and study the bear population. It was with anticipation that my long-time sidekick and adventurer, Dr. Carter Cloyd, and I prepared for another den-outing.

On a chilly March morning we accompanied a pair of bear biologists for a trek through the dense forests of central Pennsylvania. This isn't trail hiking – it's more like stumbling and tripping over snow-covered roots, rocks and twigs. An hour of this feels like a day's worth of normal hiking. "Almost there," one biologist said. Dr. Cloyd and I exchanged doubtful glances. There's a difference between a city almost there and a forest almost there. I don't know how many times we were almost there, but eventually we did arrive at the den. Peeking inside we saw that all was quiet. It was perfect. The lead biologist loaded his rifle with a tranquilizer dart and aimed into the den. This wouldn't hurt the mama bear – It was just to insure that she'd sleep during our visit. In a perfect world, that is. The rifle made a sharp crack and the dart found its mark, but mama bear, startled, charged past us into the woods. "There she goes!" I said, but Dr. Cloyd, who had been close to the den opening, was still in shock. The thought of being run over by a quarter-ton fur ball still registered on his face. He gave me an admonishing look that seemed to say, "How do I let you talk me into these things? Only with you could this go wrong – twice!" The same thing had happened to us on a prior bear expedition. The biologists began explaining what had to be done now, but we already knew the drill. They would have to track down the mama while Dr.Cloyd and I babysat the cubs.

Poking my head into the den I was amazed at bear housekeeping. The den was very clean and odor-free. Inside, we were surprised to find four cubs! The national average is only two, Pennsylvania's average is three, but this den had been blessed with four. With the help of one biologist, we got the cubs and ourselves situated before he and his partner went off after the mother. Dr. Cloyd and I each held two cubs. Mine cuddled quietly under my warm down jacket, but his cubs whined and wailed like babies that needed to be fed or changed. Perhaps they sensed his nervousness about the possibility of the mother returning. His eyes darted about in the hope that the biologist would be the first one back to the den. I wasn't worried. "This hibernation thing is great," I said as I nestled my body down onto the ground. "I think I'll take a nap."

"You think you'll do what?" he responded nervously. "Are you nuts?" But our encounter with these cubs brought me a real sense of peace. I got to enjoy the best nap I ever had, with two teddy bears on my chest while Dr. Cloyd kept watch. As I drifted off to sleep, thoughts of protecting these wonderful animals danced in my head. "Their habitat needs to be protected," I mused. Education will continue to be one of the biggest aids in helping wildlife to thrive safely. People need to be aware that bears are not vicious killing machines. That image may make exciting movies, but the reality is that bears need to be respected, not feared. Black bears are omnivores just like us. They prefer to take the easier route, scavenging when possible, and finding their meals instead of hunting. This is the source of the problems between humans and bears. We both consider it our right to live in the woods. Then, when our garbage isn't put into bear-proof bins or properly disposed of, the black bears come around. Bears eventually become unafraid of people, seeing them as easy marks for a handout. Associating trash with food, they become garbage addicts, making them unhealthy and lazy. The homes of careless humans become the bears' fast food drive-through, making humans an obstacle between them and their next meal. This puts both species into potentially dangerous situations. Fortunately, there hasn't been a fatality in Pennsylvania due to bears in more than a century, but if they feel they are threatened, bears may defend themselves. Getting between a bear and her food is dangerous. Worse is getting between a female bear and her cubs. Like any human parent, she will protect them.

Pennsylvania has done an amazing job with bears. With a little education we can all live in harmony with these wonderful creatures. Merely disposing of trash properly would eliminate most of the negative interactions between people and bears. Traditionally, farmers and predator animals have been at odds, going as far as poisoning campaigns against some of the larger species. Since 1945, though, Pennsylvania farmers have been reimbursed for crops, livestock or beehives that are destroyed by black bears. "Each case is carefully researched," says Northeast Region conservationist, Joe Wenzel. "We help the farmers, but they have to help us too. Farmers who kill bears receive no compensation." Wenzel further says that the state budgets $50,000 for fencing to help farmers and beekeepers protect their livelihoods. In addition, Pennsylvania closely monitors and regulates hunting practices. It is still permissible to hunt bear, but only under "fair" conditions. The use of bait or poison is illegal, as is killing bears in their dens or running them down with dogs. Fines from $500 to $1500 have been introduced for the illegal killing of a black bear, and courts can make poachers pay restitution of $800 to $5000, depending upon the size and sex of the animal. All of this has served to increase the bear population.

But ignorance remains. People unfamiliar with nature hold unrealistic and silly expectations. I recalled some city people renting one of my neighbor's homes in the Poconos. They just didn't get it! They called the game commission to complain about black bears in the nearby woods. "Get these bears out of here," the panicky visitors complained. I remembered shaking my head in disbelief as I asked the commissioner, "So how did you handle it? Did you tell the renters that they were the ones who'd have to leave?" It is a wonderful gift to have communities dedicated to living in peaceful coexistence with wildlife. The biggest challenge still remains, though – protecting the bears' habitat. Builders have to be sensitive to the landscape and not indiscriminately clear forested areas that might provide the bears' food source. In Pennsylvania there are "earth disturbance" ordinances in areas where bear populations exist, and there is tax leniency for those who agree to limit development. Preservation organizations such as Clean and Green, Nature Conservancy and Wild Land Conservancy all help protect the bears' habitat, but it is just as important that individuals do their part.

"Dayne. Dayne! Wake up, Dayne. You're talking in your sleep."

Dr. Cloyd was shaking me. I had taken a longer nap than I intended.

"It's getting dark and the biologists still haven't come back," he warned. We discussed our options. Should we wait, even until it was completely dark? Should we return to the truck? If we returned to the truck, should we leave the cubs on their own? No, I reasoned, we can't leave the cubs alone. Luckily, we didn't have to make a decision. While we were debating, one of the biologists entered the den. He looked exhausted. They had tracked the mother bear through the forest for a mile. To protect the drugged animal, the lead biologist had instructed his assistant to construct a makeshift den while he returned for us. It was decided that we would take the cubs back to the truck and drive them to the temporary den where they would be reunited with their mother. They would all wake up to a forest home makeover. I tried to imagine what Mama Bear would think when she saw her new home. A forest without bears is like a city without people. I only hope that humans will see the value of these animals and learn to co-exist with them.

◊ GENESIS 1:25-26 *God made the wild animals according to their kinds, the livestock according to their kinds, and all the creatures that move along the ground according to their kinds. And God saw that it was good.*

FLY FISHING?
IF POP COULD SEE ME NOW!

"**P**op! Pop, pull it up. Pull it up!" I'd be with my grandfather in our secret spot on the bay at Wildwood, New Jersey. He made me promise not to tell anybody where it was.

"Not yet, Dayne, not yet. We just put it in. You've gotta be patient when you're crabbing. They're kind of slow, ya know. You gotta give 'em time."

"No, Pop, pull it up now! I know we caught one!" My grandfather was teaching me a lesson. I'd discover that, except for the fresh fish heads he'd tied down as bait, the crab nets were still empty. Patience was something I lacked. With all the time in the world ahead of me, I wanted it to move faster. With a little of Pop's patience forced upon me, though, we'd start to pull up two or three crabs at a time. With a little patience, we'd have plenty of crab to flavor the gravy that night. With a little patience, on our best outing we caught a record twenty-one crabs, and the record still stands! I loved crabbing with Poppy. It's one of my fondest childhood memories.

As a kid I was a little squeamish. I wouldn't touch the fish heads – I made Pop tie the bait in the nets. And cleaning the crabs? No way! Just the thought of cracking shells and breaking off claws made me cringe. I didn't want to have to do the dirty work.

"What kind of a crabber are you?" Pop lovingly mocked. There's more to crabbing than just pulling up the nets!

Pop's passed away now. He left the shore home to me. It's been updated so it can be rented out, but in the shed, the nets have been left as they had always been. I tell the renters, "Enjoy the home, but just don't touch the crab nets on the left side of the shed. That's one of the rules." When I check on the house from time to time that's the first place I go, and when I see those nets, I remember those special times with Pop.

Now, decades later, Pop's squeamish grandson was trying his hand in the eccentric world of fly fishing. If Pop could only see me now! If crabbing is "blue collar," then fly fishing is the top of the corporate ladder. And I still don't want to do the dirty work.

Fly fishermen are a different breed. To others, these fellows appear to be elitist fanatics, standing in their picturesque streams, wearing their picturesque outfits, waving their picturesque rods about, but make no mistake – they are some of the most genuine and sincere people you'll ever meet. And this sport is far from being merely picturesque. It takes real skill, a lot of knowledge, and much practice. These outdoorsmen might spend literally hours staring through a magnifying glass at the fly that they're tying in a tiny little vise, trying to imitate nature's wonders. They'll use special intricate knots to tie the fly on the leader, the leader to the fly line. It's craftsmanship. It's art. And ultimately, it's a very serious contest with a fish. Fly fishermen are among the most intense sportsmen imaginable. Without a proper respect for their sport, an outsider would have a hard time getting into their fascinating culture. With the right attitude, though, they'll welcome you in and give you the privilege of seeing a world that's usually viewed only from a picturesque distance.

Nature's beauty enthralls me and fly fishing fits right in: You get the opportunity to be in the thick of the action, actually becoming a part of the landscape. You're out there in God's creation, dressed in sporty attire, constantly moving and casting, involved in an intense contest. I love the challenge of pitting my skills against a tricky opponent. And with "catch and release," the fish is rewarded for having put up a good fight. And as far as eccentricity goes, I've been called that a few times, so I fit right in. But compared to fervent fly fishermen, I'm still just a hacker.

I began working on my fly fishing credentials several years ago in my hometown by visiting Barry at The Sporting Gentleman, the local Orvis shop.

He was a walking historian of the sport. He spoke enthusiastically about the sport that he was so knowledgeable and passionate about, and he smiled slyly when I said I was looking for professional instruction.

"I've got just the person for you, Dayne," he said. I thought I was going to meet another white-haired, bearded gentleman – or maybe a John Muir type. What I got, though, was Mary. Mary was her name and fly fishing was her game! She was a knowledgeable, respected angler and a real technician too. Barry and Mary set me straight with a brief history and an accurate picture of the sport.

"Although it goes back to first century," Barry began, "the art of what we now call fly fishing evolved over the last couple of centuries in England. The object of the sport is to trick a nervous, wary fish into biting onto a fly that you've gently and accurately placed in its path from a distance."

But the sport is more than just buying a fancy rod and reel.

"Depending on the variety of fish you're after, the sort of food the fish likes, the current and the wind conditions, you might want your line to float on the water's surface, or sink slightly, or sink deeper. For given conditions, with the right combination of rod, fly line, leader and fly, the equipment becomes an extension of the fisherman's arm. It enables him to place the fly on the water so gently that it barely ripples the surface."

If this all sounds confusing, understand that it's just the tip of the iceberg!

There are so many variables! Even after learning the skills to use the equipment, there's a general knowledge of the prey that's needed. The fish's field of vision is different than a man's – you have to make yourself invisible to the fish. You also need to be quiet – sounds traveling through the water will warn the fish of danger. The time of year also determines whether the fish's favorite insect-food is in the larval, the pupal, or the adult stage. That determines what sort of fly should be used, and whether the leader should float or sink. Also, depending on the time of year or the time of day, the water temperature affects the fish's willingness to come to the surface for food. Depending on the variety of fish you're sporting, you might be fishing in the sun or in the shade, in still water, in a fast-running stream, or anything in between. This also affects the choice of lines and flies, with names like Blacknose Dace, Muddler Minnow, Woolly Bugger and McGinnis Extra Stout. It sounded mindboggling, but I was up to the challenge – if I could handle it in my own way.

Then in my mind I heard the voice of my grandfather.

"Who are you kidding, Dayne?" he was gently mocking. "You don't even like to touch a fish! I know that you like the action, but I don't think you have the patience for all this."

"Aw, Pop," I heard myself answer, "I didn't have the patience then, and I still don't have it, but I've got a method. I'll find a good guide and he'll show me the ropes. I'll leave the details to the pro. He'll select the right fly. He'll tie it on the leader with the right knot. Heck, if I'm lucky, he might even take the fish off the hook for me. I'll catch and he'll release."

It was true; I didn't want to be bogged down with frustrating preparation and details at this point For now I just wanted to cast and catch – like in the pictures. I knew that in time I could pick up more of the other skills.

After some starter lessons casting with a fly rod on grass, Mary and I moved to the local state parks, casting from the banks of the creeks. Here we caught sunnies and small mouthed bass, and I learned the proper etiquette of fly fishing. Eventually, I was graduated to wearing waders and fishing in the middle of creeks. This gave me a different perspective on fly-fishing, becoming a part of the scene rather than just an observer. Under Mary's guidance, I began to share in the experience and the challenge. Then, with the help of some other guides, my skills rose to a level respectable enough to try my hand at fishing in the Poconos. What I really wanted, though, was to take this new found love to my favorite playground, my favorite landscape, Wyoming. This is what Mary and I had been building up to.

It was in Wyoming that I met Spencer. Spencer, a true sportsman, had been raised in Vermont. He had hunted elk, he had hiked through South America, he had been a fly fishing guide in Alaska, and now in Wyoming, he became my guide and friend. I told him that, although I didn't have much experience fly fishing, I'd fished in the Shoshone River and in Buffalo Valley. We took an instant liking to each other, fishing for a couple of days on the Snake River. I think he liked my spunk and spirit.

"You really seem to like the sport," he said. "If you have another day, I think I've got a treat for you. I'll take you to a beautiful spot that I know of, just a few miles outside of Jackson. I think you'll get a kick out of it. But you have to promise to keep it a secret. Otherwise, it's no deal. It's the perfect spot – great view of the Tetons, crystal clear water, wildlife everywhere…"

He didn't have to say any more. I was sold. So it was that we trekked through wild Wyoming terrain to the most gorgeous secret spot I had ever seen – along the clear, cold, rushing current of the Snake River.

"Pop, I wish you could be with me now!" I thought. "The beauty of this scene makes you reflect on God and His creation."

Standing in a sunny bend of the river I practiced the rhythmic motion of casting with a few false casts – no sense needlessly spooking the prey. But next to Spencer I felt like a rookie.

"Just don't make yourself look foolish," I told myself.

"Relax," Spencer said, handing me the rod he had just prepared. "Do it like you've practiced. Go over there and start casting."

As he turned to prepare another rod, I waded silently downstream, got firm footing and stripped out some line. The wind was blowing and my first few casts missed the mark. I started to feel really clumsy and self-conscious.

"Patience, Dayne," he called softly. It was just like a voice from long ago, and my nerves began to settle down. About twenty-five feet away was a likely spot – a large rock near a point that jutted out from the river bank. I suspected that my trout would be over there looking for his lunch, and I didn't want to keep him waiting. Mentally calculating the distance and wind and current, I caught lightning in a bottle – a perfect cast! The fly was presented gently on the water just a bit upstream from the rock. In the corner of my eye I noticed that Spencer had seen my cast. So far so good! The fly drifted only a few feet when suddenly, Bang! I had a strike! When I set the hook, something on my line started pulling like a tractor! Spencer watched in disbelief. Thanks to good weather, good luck and great instructors, the rookie from Philly reeled in the catch of the day – a native cut throat trout, twenty-one inches long! Twenty-one inches, Pop, just like the twenty-one crabs! Yeah! That's the way it's done!

◊ GENESIS 1:20,21, *28 God said, "Let the water teem with living creatures...so He created the great creatures of the sea and every living and moving thing with which the water teems, according to their kind. God blessed the man and woman and said to them,..."fill the earth and subdue it, and rule over the fish of the sea."*

THE GREAT DAYNE

I have always been fascinated by magicians and the amazing illusions they perform. Often, an illusion is nothing more than a diversion of the audience's attention from what is really going on. While they're watching the smoke and mirrors, the trick has already been done! An illusion may involve an elaborate construction; some fantastic mechanical thing that plays upon the viewers' senses and logic, but these inventions don't work as we're made to believe. We assume that the contraption is doing one thing, while it's actually doing something else. In the best performances, the audience knows that the magician is trying to fool them, so they watch closely, only to be fooled anyway. That's the fun of it.

My fascination with magic started because of my mother. She was an old-movie buff, and one particular Friday night, after popping the popcorn and preparing snacks, we watched Tony Curtis playing the part of Harry Houdini. What a character! I was hooked! Today, Houdini is universally regarded as the father of magic, and his name is synonymous with escapes. But this didn't come easily. Houdini was born in poverty in Budapest, Hungary in 1874 and came to America as a boy. He was small man – only 5 ft 5 inches, but he was very athletic. Harry was highly motivated to succeed and he had a knack for publicity that would make Madison Avenue jealous. After seeing the most famous magician of his day, Dr. Lynn, Harry decided by age 17 to learn the craft. He tried all aspects of magic. He learned dexterity with cards, and manipulations, and illusions, and he was a contortionist – a skill that came in handy when he began his escape acts. He was able to astound an audience with his "needle illusion" – swallowing twenty threaded needles, and regurgitating them back, all threaded on the same thread. But he wasn't having the success he had hoped for. After five years of struggling, he was ready to sell all of his equipment for $20.00. The turning point for him was his "Challenge Act." He challenged all comers to try to keep him in a pair of handcuffs. By 1904 he was the "Handcuff King." This was the beginning of his spectacular escapes. He escaped from jail cells and from padlocked crates thrown in the river. He was buried alive. He escaped from a water torture cell. Suspended upside down hundreds of feet in the air he escaped from a straightjacket. There seemed to be nothing that could hold him prisoner, and he became a legend in his own time.

My grandfather heard that we had seen the Houdini movie and, not to be outdone, he told me that he had a card trick of his own with a clever twist. After selecting a card from Pop's deck and showing it to him, he would telephone a mysterious man called "Mr. Wizard". Mr. Wizard, he said, was a rich old man who lived in a mansion with servants, and he had the ability to identify the card I had picked. Here is how the phone call went.

Pop: "Hello, may I speak with Mr. Wizard please? Yes, I'll wait." (And then, speaking to me with his hand over the mouthpiece) "It's his butler – he's going to get him." And then, just a moment later, "Hello, Mr. Wizard, I have someone here who has just picked a card from my deck." and Pop handed me the phone. In a stern voice Mr. Wizard said to me, "Your card is the king of hearts," and he hung up abruptly. And don't you know, I had picked the king of hearts! After years of pestering Poppy, he finally taught me how to do "Mr. Wizard," but he swore me to secrecy. It's a very serious code of honor among magicians. I had a lot of fun performing "Mr. Wizard" for my friends and acquaintances.

I've even been accused of having secret microphones and hidden cameras, but nobody has ever successfully guessed how it was done.

That's a fond memory from a long time ago. Poppy's gone now, but I still haven't grown up. Recently, I had a chance to bring some magic to my friends, and I couldn't pass up the chance to do a little performing myself. At the time, I was the head of the evangelism committee at my church. I know what you're thinking - they must have been desperate. We were planning a community outreach and were looking for a creative way to draw people in. I recalled seeing a clever Christian magician, Charles Wormsley, who interwove his magic with a presentation of the Gospel in a way that was at the same time un-intimidating, fun, and true to the Word. It was just the sort of thing we needed.

I contacted Mr. Wormsley and offered to take him to dinner to discuss a proposal. We met at a diner on Broad Street, and by the end of the meal he was delighted to visit our church and do his act. "Actually, I was hoping for a bit more," I stammered. "I'm supposed to be the emcee, but I'd like to be a part of the show too. Do you think you could squeeze me into something – no pun intended."

"Gosh, Dayne, I don't know about that," he said. "I work solo, you know. But I have an idea…"

He offered to introduce me to another magician who had a warehouse full of illusions. He might, or might not, be willing to share some of his secrets. A meeting was set up and I got to meet The Great Garibaldi, who was guarded and secretive. He wouldn't let me wander around his warehouse, but he was willing to show me a few things that I might use for the performance.

He explained, "There's more to this than just doing tricks - a trick isn't an act. Anybody can pull a rabbit from a hat. You have to sell the illusion. You need to hook the audience and reel them in. An illusion," he explained, "is a dramatization. It has a beginning, a middle, and an climax." For a couple of hours, we talked about how the great illusionists spend years polishing their skills and perfecting their craft, and he was willing to teach me how to turn a couple of basic ploys into an actual act for our evening of evangelism. "Break a leg," he told me as I left his lair.

The big night was upon us! The event had been well publicized in Houdini style, and hundreds turned out. I took the role of emcee in typical Dayne Traveler fashion, dressed in black tux and tails, top hat, and white gloves. I had to look the part! I welcomed the audience and informed them that, in addition to our featured guest, I would also be performing this evening. The audience seemed unconvinced.

For my first illusion I pulled a deck of cards from my pocket. "May I have a volunteer from the audience?" I asked, shuffling the cards mid-air.

A uniformed policeman rose from the crowd – he didn't look amused.

"I have to stop you here," he said angrily. "You can't be doing card tricks and magic in a church. You're under arrest!" And he quickly came forward, snapped a pair of handcuffs on my wrists, and led me past the shocked audience toward the door.

"You have the right to remain silent…" The audience watched in disbelief.

"You can't handcuff me like this," I protested.

"What makes you think I can't?" he challenged. With a Houdini like flourish I deftly slipped out of the handcuffs.

"Your handcuffs just aren't strong enough to stop the Gospel," I replied.

The audience suddenly realized that a joke had been played upon them and they laughed and applauded loudly. I introduced the "officer" – he was a friend who had agreed to help out this night. So far, so good!

I announced, "I really will need a volunteer now."

Another man came forward.

"For the sake of the audience," I said, "do we know each other? You're not another 'plant', are you? Are you a part of this act in any way?"

The stranger replied that he was not – he was just someone who lived in the neighborhood and came out to see the show. Then a large, sturdy wooden stock was rolled out.

"I'm going to lock you in the stocks," I informed him. "I need you to verify for the audience that they're quite real – that you really can't get out." He willingly placed his wrists and neck into the stocks, the top was lowered and bolted shut, and four padlocks were secured. "OK, let's see if you can get out," I instructed.

He pushed and pulled and twisted and struggled, giving his escape a valiant attempt, but it was pointless. There was obviously no way for him to escape. After about a minute, he was ready to give up.

"Do you agree that these stocks are real?" I asked.

"Oh yeah, absolutely," he said humbly. I unlocked the locks, unfastened the bolts and released him, but as he started back to his seat, rubbing his wrists, I told him that I still needed his help.

"Now it's my turn," I said. Now you can put me in the stocks." As my volunteer proceeded to lock me in the stocks, I told the story of the Apostle Peter, in prison at midnight, chained between two soldiers, with a sentry at the door. An angel appeared in the cell, woke Peter, and said, 'Quick, get up!' The chains fell off Peter's wrists, and he walked out of the prison. "That's the way it is with the Gospel," I said. "There's nothing that can prevent it from reaching someone's heart." Now I was locked in the stocks. I made an obvious show of struggling to pull my hands out. "Looks like you've got me," I told the volunteer. "Now if you'll be so kind, please hold up that black sheet in front of the stocks, and I'll see if I can get out by the count of ten." He stood before me and raised the large sheet high overhead with both hands, blocking the audience's view. "Oh, one more thing," I said. "Lower the sheet a moment."

He lowered his arms, and there I stood, already out of the stocks. The audience stared in disbelief. There was a moment of surprise and then much applause. The Great Dayne was born ! Ah, how I love the spotlight! This magician stuff was really fun! Harry would be proud. I could tell you how I did it, but you know how it is with us magicians – I'm sworn to secrecy!

It was a great start to a great evening. Charles Wormsley performed his magic act, many were entertained and some heard the Good News for the first time. As gratifying as the evening was for me, I realized what I had done was just an illusion. It doesn't compare to the actual miracle that God works in transforming the heart of a new believer.

◊   ISAIAH 52:7 *How beautiful on the mountain are the feet of those who bring good tidings, who proclaim salvation, who say to Zion, "Your God reigns."*

Birds of a Feather
Hunt Together

It was a chilly but bright winter morning as I sat by the fire, fantasizing about what sort of adventure to undertake. A wanna-be sportsman like Dayne Traveler can't just lie around when there are challenges to be met. A man should be out and about doing something daring. The breadwinner should be out there, well, winning bread. It's become so easy – you go down to the store, pick up an already prepared banquet, plop it in the microwave, and in just a moment, voila, a feast. But it wasn't always so simple. It used to be that a man would gird up his loins for battle with the elements and with nature. He had to go out and subdue his dinner. But people don't do that anymore, do they? Ah, yes, some do!

Dwight Lasure is a family man and a Bible scholar, but he's also Dwight, the falconer – that's right, falconer. He hunts with a raptor on his wrist. I gave Dwight a call to see if I could interview him and, hopefully, go along with him on an outing. He said yes! "But are you sure you've got what it takes?" he asked. "These aren't parakeets, you know."

"For me, Falconry is a passion," he told me. "It's only after you get through a maze of apprenticeship that you're free to trap your first bird of prey. And then you have to train it to hunt with you. It's no armchair sport!" Dwight described the steps in training a winged killing machine. "Falconry is unlike any other hunting sport. You might catch a bird of prey and train it, but then you have to convince it to be your hunting partner. And although the bird only weighs two or three pounds, if you mishandle it, it has ways of getting even! Training one takes steady nerves. There's nothing like trapping your first bird! You're hiding there in a camouflaged cover on top of a mountain, waiting with a baited bownet trap. Through a slit you can see eagles, falcons and hawks of all sorts, small specks in the sky. It's just a matter of time before one spots the bait. About a half mile away, one will tuck and turn and shoot in like a missile at about a hundred miles an hour. Suddenly there's a flash of feathers, and you've got an angry bird tangled in your net. Now you've got to figure how to free it without getting torn up! Once it's out of the trap, a hood is put over its head. This helps to calm the bird by eliminating visual stimulation. Then the talons have to be taped. After the bird is dusted for lice and feather mites, it's slipped into a lady's stocking (minus the toes). This is a gentle way of trussing up the bird to keep it from hurting itself. You might trap several more birds, looking for a really good one, but it isn't a beauty contest. I keep the aggressive ones with big feet and let the others go. Then comes the long training process.

"The bird is taken immediately to a darkened shed called a mews to calm down for the next twelve hours. It's sitting free, in the dark, on a perch. Periodically, I'll check on it with nothing but a penlight, and the next day I'll sit quietly next to it in the dark for maybe four hours. The bird can sense your presence, but it won't attack in the dark. This is the way we build trust, and the bird gets used to me. It's a bit risky. The next day, still in the dark, I'll bring in a tidbit in my gloved hand. When I shine the penlight on the tidbit, the hawk can accept the food from me or not. Typically, within one to three days, a hawk will take food from the hand. My hawk was a real Jezebel. She took five days! Once she started to cooperate and became more ladylike, I renamed her Belle. First, she began taking food from me at her perch. Then, the next day I moved farther away. By day six, she was showing the positive gesture of coming toward me. By day eight she would fly from the perch to my gloved hand. After two and a half months she was trained. The rule of thumb is that if you think the bird is ready to fly free, spend another two weeks flying it on a creance line. It should be able to fly at least a hundred yards on the line before flying free. At that point you just keep increasing the distances.

"Next, the bird has to be wed to its prey. A live animal, usually a store-bought rabbit or mouse, is placed under a bush. Then I return to my Jeep and get the bird. I walk through the woods toward the bait, kicking up the brush as I go with the bird following behind, flying from tree to tree. When I frighten the bait from its hiding place, the bird's natural hunting instinct takes over. Its reward is that it's allowed to eat as much of the prey as it wants. Then I offer the bird a tidbit to bring it back, and we go home. School's out!" For me it was just beginning.

I could picture it now – Dayne Falconer, dressed in manly British tweeds in search of his dinner. What could be better! What could improve upon that image? Maybe a partner! Yeah, that's it – me and my sidekick cruising through the mountains in my Aston Martin, on a dangerous mission, just like James Bond. Just then my cell phone rang. I flipped it open nonchalantly and responded,

"This is Traveler, Dayne Traveler...what? Who's this? Oh, Suzie! Hey, Suzie, how are you doing?"

Suzanne Elizabeth Foster, a graduate of Moorlands College in England; attractive and intelligent, she earned her degree in applied theology. She'd done missionary work in Papua New Guinea, and had spent a year in Uganda with Youth With A Mission. "We're talking mud huts, here" she says. Suzie had traveled over six continents, and she'd lived out of her one suitcase on three of them. She's passionate and, obviously, an adventurer too - and she definitely had the accent! She had been hinting to me about coming along on an adventure, and here was the opportunity. I'd invite Suzie. She'd make a perfect partner – Suzie Sidekick. I loved it!

The morning of our outing I picked up Suzanne in my Corvette. It wasn't quite an Aston Martin, but it was the best America had to offer. I was sporting my worn felt hat, and my outfit of muted browns and tans was just woolen and tweedy enough to pass for British. Suzie had disappointed me, though. She was wearing faded jeans, a nylon windbreaker and Nikes. Perhaps I hadn't sufficiently explained the mission. Still, the two hour ride to the mountains was a pleasure, marked by animated conversation and the steady growl of the engine. When we roared up to our destination, Dwight waved and indicated where we were to park. I pulled off the road onto an area of winter-brown grass and mud where Dwight gave me a curious look.

"I don't suppose that's four-wheel drive, is it?" he chuckled. "Some adventurer you are, Dayne, going hunting in a 'Vette!"

Dwight transported us further into the fields in his Jeep. Suzie and I shared the ride with Belle, the red-tailed hawk. Belle was in her "giant hood" – a large darkened box. Along the way I had a chance to learn more about the sport of falconry.

"Could you teach anybody to do this?" I asked.

"That depends," Dwight replied. "They'd have to be patient, and be able to put up with pain too - raptors bite, and they can rake you with their talons. One big question would be, 'Are they emotionally prepared to hunt?' Falconry is sharing your life with a creature that's evolved over eons to do just one thing - kill. Squeamish stomachs can't hack it. And then, after putting in all the time and effort to train a bird, you have to understand that, at any moment of free flight, it may choose to simply fly away. The sport's not for everyone."

"This looks like the place," Dwight said, rolling to a stop and slipping his hand into his heavy leather glove, the gauntlet. When he opened the giant hood and reached in, Belle hopped right onto the gauntlet. Drawing her out, he released her with a slight toss, and she flew into the branches of a nearby tree.

"Now what," I asked.

"Now we trudge," was the answer. The three of us fanned out and began walking through the brush, rustling the grass and bushes to flush out any prey. All the while, Belle watched with eagle eyes – well, hawk eyes – for any action. After we had traveled about fifty yards, Dwight called Belle, and she flew to a closer tree. Then we began again. Suzie and Dwight were chatting, both of them eager for some action. She wanted to see a rabbit lose its head! I wasn't so sure now. What if I roused up some innocent little bunny – I'd have bunny-blood on my hands for eternity!

"You look like you're tiptoeing through the tulips, Dayne!" Suzie mocked.

"C'mon, Dayne," Dwight chimed in, "what kind of a hunter are you? You've got a reputation to maintain here!"

"This is me maintaining my reputation," I answered. "I might not be all I'm cracked up to be." As we trudged and kicked and kicked and trudged, Belle would reposition herself high behind us along the way. We weren't having any luck, though.

"We ought to change locations," Dwight suggested, and we circled back to the Jeep. Then, after a short drive, we started all over again.

"OK, Dayne, now it's your turn," Dwight said. "Put the gauntlet on and reach right in there. She knows what to do."

"Piece of cake," I replied. The gauntlet was heavier than I had imagined. As I reached toward the giant hood, Dwight added, "Now don't show any fear or hesitation, or she'll sense it and tear you up!"

"Whoa, there!" I said. "Maybe you should do this." Those were not the words to impress Suzie.

"What? You wuss!" she mocked. "I'll never let you live this down!"

Now I had to do it. I put on my most confident face, reached in and waited. Belle eyed me suspiciously, but decided to go along for the ride. Once she was out, I held her as far away as I could, very conscious of her sharp talons and my handsome, unmarred face.

"If you hold her any farther away and she'll be free," Suzie joked.

"Now what?" I asked, ignoring her.

"OK, squat down, put the gauntlet on the ground and slide your hand out. We'll give Suzanne a turn too." Suzie was all too eager. She got down and fearlessly slipped her hand in, lifted Belle and, holding Belle close, admired her markings and size. I think Belle liked the flattery.

"Go ahead and fly her," Dwight suggested, and like an experienced falconer, Suzie imitated Dwight's toss. Belle soared high into the trees.

"That's incredible!" she said excitedly. "I feel just like Robin Hood!"

I think she meant to say "Maid Marion."

We didn't have any luck hunting that day. Dwight and Suzie were disappointed but I only pretended to be. I think they were on to me, though

"I don't suspect the Dayne Falconer Club will be increasing its membership anytime soon," Dwight laughed.

Still, it was a good outing and we had learned a lot. But as far as playing with dangerous birds goes, the little blond Brit outdid me. I guess it takes one tough chick to handle another.

◊   ISAIAH 41:31   *Those who hope in the Lord will renew their strength. They will soar on wings like eagles: they will run and not grow weary, they will walk and not be faint.*

JOKERS WILD

Dayne Traveler has sometimes been accused of being an adrenaline junkie. What most don't see are the daily bold attempts that are made to go beyond everyday comfort zones to experience life to the fullest. It just so happens that it sometimes involves intense physical activity, the occasional taking of chances and the release of adrenaline into the bloodstream. I try not to limit my adventures to distant and exotic places. Sometimes I just can't get away. The responsibilities of home and career don't always allow for travel. During these periods of "Adventure Withdraw," on-site recreation is the order of the day.

As a kid I loved the TV show, "Candid Camera", where Alan Funt would pull off some of the craziest stunts on an unsuspecting public. The jokes could be so complex and outrageous that the person would spend the longest and most embarrassing time, disbelieving that such a thing could be happening to them. Funt's basic technique was to let a gag go on and on and on until the victim had to react. Then, just at the breaking point, when tempers were ready to flare, Funt would drop his famous line, "Smile, you're on Candid Camera." I guess I was just an impressionable kid. I came to love practical jokes. And I've certainly done my share. Here are a few of my favorites.

A practical joke has to go against everything the victim knows or believes about the perpetrator to work properly. This elaborate practical joke is unbelievable on several levels. For instance, everybody knows that Dayne tries to be an honest and up-front kind of guy! He wouldn't do anything to make anyone feel ill at ease. Or would he?

The stage is conveniently set in my office. The ruse is that there's an illegal casino being run in the basement, (there is no basement) and three cohorts, who've been briefed on the gag, have crammed themselves into the closet. Enter my victim. While we're talking business, the first of my accomplices emerges from the closet.

"Dayne, I had a great time!" he says. "I even won $20 at the blackjack table. Can I cash in here?"

"Sure," I reply, opening my desk drawer in which I've placed a cash box. He hands me some chips and I give him a twenty. "Thanks for coming out," I tell him. "I'll see you next week." As you can imagine, the victim now has a question on his face, but he says nothing, refusing to believe what just transpired. We return to our conversation, only to be interrupted again by the second member of my gang.

"How'd you do tonight?" I ask her.

"Oh, not too bad," she says. "I lost a little but I had fun. You open tomorrow? I want a chance to get even."

"Nah, not tomorrow. Not on Wednesdays," I tell her. "The police come by on Wednesdays. But if you come on Thursday, I'll give you preferred parking. Here, let me stamp your parking stub. I'll cut you a break since you lost tonight."

She hands me her valet parking ticket which I stamp "paid" with a stamper from the desk drawer, and she leaves with a smile. My visitor looks bewildered by now, but I ignore his doubtful glances and continue our conversation. Then we're interrupted a third time.

"Great time, Dayne, and the buffet was terrific!"

"Did you like the show? How about those dancers! And the singer – I was lucky to sign her."

"Yeah, she's really good." he agrees. "How long will she

be here?"

"Just until Saturday," I tell him. "She'll be in town at the Walnut next week."

"Well, she's good enough," he says going out the door.

Now my visitor really has his doubts. I can almost read his mind

"What's going on?" he demands. I give him a questioning look as if I can't understand why he'd be so perturbed.

"I've got a little casino and nightclub downstairs," I tell him. "Nothing too fancy – a blackjack table and a roulette wheel, a couple of slots. One of my clients does the catering, and another one's a booking agent – he's found me a few good acts. It's no big deal. I've got to make ends meet, you know. Why? Don't you gamble?"

"Well, I've gambled before, but it was always legal. Isn't this a little risky?"

"No, it's no big deal."

"I've gotta see this." he says. (He's hooked now.)

"Go on down," I tell him. "I'll buzz them and let them know you're on your way." I can hardly keep a straight face.

When he walks into the closet my partners in crime enter laughing as the victim realized that he's been had. Hah! Gotcha!

Any time, any place, the opportunity to play a joke on someone can pop up. You've got to be ready all the time. One slow Monday night when I was itching to get into the game, I telephoned a friend. My then hi-tech phone had three-way conferencing, but this was before caller ID. I couldn't do this joke today.

"Hey, I just had an idea," I said. "Wanna have a little fun?"

"What's on your mind?" he asked. "It's a little late to be starting anything."

"Nah, it's the perfect time," I laughed. "It's payback time."

The wife of a close friend had actually had the audacity to pull off a practical joke on me. At the time I told her, "You're laughing now, but just you wait!" That was a while ago. Her guard was surely down by now, and I'd have the last laugh. I was pretty good at disguising my voice, and sometimes used this talent for fun.

"Take your pick," I told my friend, "Italian, Irish, or African?"

"Irish," he said.

"OK, here goes." I put on my best Irish accent – not too heavy, but just enough to be convincing – and dialed my victim. It was 11:45 at night. After half a dozen rings, she answered the phone. I signaled my friend to listen in.

"Is this Mrs. James?" I asked in a businesslike manner.

"Yes, who's this," she asked angrily. The late hour bothered her.

"This is Midnight Construction. I just wanted to let you know that we're running a little behind tonight, but we should be there in about twenty minutes."

"You're coming here? At this hour? Are you sure you've called the right number?" (My friend covered his phone so he wouldn't be heard chuckling.)

"Yes, M'am, I think so. You're John's wife, aren't you? He said you were getting fed up with your kitchen cabinets, and we're the solution to your problem. We'll be right over – rip out the old and ring in the new. We'll finish up by four." My friend rolled his eyes with incredulity.

"Four? In the morning? Are you crazy?"

No, M'am, we're Midnight Construction. We work at night. Most people aren't comfortable with workers in their homes during the day when they're at work. We provide this service at no extra cost."

"You're not coming over here at midnight," she said firmly. You'll have to schedule your work during the daytime. Around here we sleep at night."

"But this is Midnight Construction, M'am. John's contracted us to do the work, and tonight's the night. Don't worry. We'll try to keep the noise down and we'll be gone by morning."

And then began a litany of explicatives and beratings and belittlings that would make a sailor blush. It went on and on until finally I broke down with laughter. When I revealed my identity my friend suddenly realized she'd been taken in.

"You jerk," she laughed. "I'll get you back for this!"

"That's not allowed," I say in my finest Irish accent. "You're the one who started this – you should have known better than to mess with Dayne O'Traveler."

Ah, the joy of it! And it was free entertainment for my friend. Payback is beautiful.

Here's a stunt that backfired. I was in a long stretch between adventures, but I needed a fun-fix. My fascination with the inner workings of the mind puts me into contact with some pretty unusual people, and I have to admit that I find some of them amusing. When I was writing my previous book I had been interviewing a woman with (how shall I say this) an extremely Gothic lifestyle. She told me that if I was really interested, I should come to a nearby pub that her peculiar friends had rented out for a big Friday night meeting. I was on really unfamiliar ground here, and wasn't quite sure what to do. On one hand, it could be harmless fun, but on the other hand – well, let's just say that I didn't feel comfortable around these dark, bizarre characters. I could use a trusted sidekick here, and maybe I could kill a couple birds with the one stone. This could be an opportunity to play a trick on my editor. David was completely reliable. What I knew of him personally said that he was a real straight shooter – no vices, upright and moral. He was supposed to be unflappable! I decided to see if I could get a rise out of him. I had already invited him to a relaxing weekend in the Poconos to work on my book, so before our trip to the cabin I'd tell him I needed to make a little side trip. Without informing him where we were going, I'd take him to the Gothic gathering.

Friday night arrived. After starting out for the mountains, I told him we needed to make an unscheduled stop. To my surprise, he didn't even ask me where we were going. We entered the pub. It was a dingy little hole in the wall that was deliberately darkened. Inside was an assortment of strangely-dressed characters who eyed us suspiciously, until I was recognized and greeted by my interviewee. Their meeting would be held on the main floor – It turned out that the back room was for dancing. My hostess was actually very educated and interesting, and she proved to be very charming (in a Gothic sort of way.) After I relaxed a bit, I figured it was time to embarrass David. Since he knew that I didn't drink, I asked, "Can I buy you guys some drinks?" sure to get a raised eyebrow from him. She wanted a Bloody Mary, of course – I should have seen that one coming.

Without batting an eye, David said, "Sure, I'll have one too," and then he turned toward our hostess and chatted comfortably with her. I guess this was a case of 'When in Rome...'

David wasn't at all intimidated by her black fingernails, her blood-red lips, her sharp fangs (no kidding) or by the dark surroundings.

"Who does your dental work," he teased. He was as charming and at ease as she was, joking, even flirting with our hostess. This scheme wasn't turning out quite as I had pictured it.

Since it was getting close to Thanksgiving, there was a buffet of everyone's Thanksgiving favorites – apparently, these characters preferred turkey with stuffing over blood sausage – and there was an impressive assortment of pies. In the far corner was a table of home-baked goods that were for sale – the proceeds would go to a wolf sanctuary. (Go figure) Then the meeting began. We all took our seats and what followed was more like a committee meeting than anything I had expected. One officer read the minutes of their previous meeting; another one gave the financial figures for the month; there was even an informative little lecture about their bizarre lifestyle. Except for the macabre dance music they had chosen, and their intimidating appearance, they were actually a docile group of people. David seemed to feel right at home. His ability to roll with the punches surprised me. Some practical joke this had turned out to be!

On our way up the turnpike to the Poconos I confessed that I had expected a little shock and dismay on David's part - not the ease and familiarity he showed.

"I was surprised that you didn't get flustered," I told him, "that you didn't think I was crazy."

"Are you kidding?" he answered, "I'm the guy who helps you tell your stories. Nothing you do could surprise me. You'll have to try harder next time, Dayne. I know you too well."

"Help me to understand this," I said. "Do you think these people basically play Halloween 365 days a year? And if that's all it is, why was I so suspicious of the gathering, while you took it all in stride?"

"It's not hard to understand, Dayne," he told me. "You've read the passage often enough: 'Love drives out fear.' You mustn't let their scary getups prevent you from seeing that there's a needy soul inside. They just want to be loved and accepted like everyone else. Sure, they're misguided. Sure, they're a bit off course. But so were we before we trusted in Christ. You'll never bring them closer to the Lord by fearing them or chasing them away."

With the sounds of "Monster Mash" still in my head, I thought I heard a mocking voice that sounded like Alan Funt. This backfired practical joke turned out to be more of a lesson than I could have expected.

◊   1st JOHN 4:18 *There is no fear in love. But perfect love drives out fear, because fear has to do with punishment. The one who fears is not made perfect in love.*

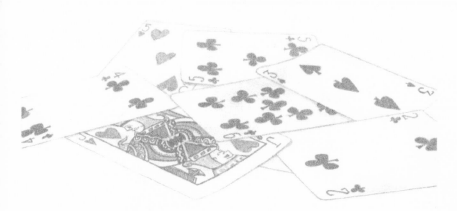

READY FOR SOME FOOTBALL?

We all have fantasies. One of mine has always been to be a pro quarterback. Although the Eagles are in trouble at times, I don't expect they'll be calling me anytime soon. Fortunately, there is a time that I can live out my fantasy. Thanksgiving! Sure, there's turkey, stuffing, cranberry sauce and pumpkin pie, but for me, like many, Thanksgiving is synonymous with football. For that, I'm extremely thankful. All across the country, men of all ages will assemble on Thanksgiving for a traditional game of pick-up football, and in my neck of the woods, it's called the Blue Bowl. We always play on Thanksgiving morning right after our church service.

The Blue Bowl is a 35-year tradition. On game day we don the jerseys that our wives or kids purchased for us the previous Christmas and get set to enjoy a camaraderie like no other. Even guys who moved out of the area long ago will travel back home for the annual match-up. One former Pennsylvania resident, Jeff Brown, drives up from Virginia every fall, migrating like a misguided goose. "I've been playing in the Bowl since I was a kid and wouldn't miss it for the world," he says.

Men have Peter Pan syndrome. They forget that their bodies don't move quite the way they used to. The joints aren't as flexible, they're carrying a little more weight than they should, and they seem to require more oxygen. Reality won't hit them until the next day when getting out of bed is a strenuous effort. "Did it always feel like this?" they wonder. What some of them risk by engaging in this once-a-year event is frightening. Frank DeSante, owner of a world class hair salon and spa, says, "I travel all over the world perfecting my styling skills, but it all gets put on the line Thanksgiving Day." The wise ones begin training for the game weeks in advance - like George Clark, who works for an auto dealership in Delaware. He says, "I look forward to this game all year, and begin working out in October. When the boss isn't looking, I practice my blocking against the trucks on the lot. I'll line up on a bumper, take my lineman's stance and explode off the line to try to drive the truck back as far as I can. Once I dented one of the trucks and got caught by the boss. He took it out of my pay. But by game day I was a terror!"

Yes, men from all walks of life and from all around the country will turn out for their yearly ritual - an opportunity to smell the pigskin. Many of the guys on my team only see each other on this one special occasion. Some of us gather the night before the game to reminisce about previous Blue Bowls, and to plan our strategy for the coming event because, let's face it, we really do want to win. Some people might think we're delusional, but this is our Super Bowl.

"Hey, Dayne," one teammate joked, how about the time you had that 12-year old kid play - the one who's dad was a Packer! What a game that was, eh!"

"Yeah, yeah, Jason Culbreth! I remember watching him in this kids' game and was amazed how good he was. He had absolutely blazing speed, and man, could he jump! He was only, what, about five foot two! I had to get his mom's permission for him to play in the Bowl. He was my secret weapon. I knew everybody would underestimate him."

"I remember - but it was a tough game that year - fourth quarter, tie score, final play..."

"That's right. Of all the games we've played I'll never forget that one - Backed up on the wrong side of the fifty, clock ticking down, wide receivers racing down the field, and HAIL MARY! Then up he goes - out jumps absolutely everybody, snatches the ball and lands in a heap over the goal line! Touchdown! Game over! I loved it!"

It's exhilarating, roughing it up, laughing, and hanging with the guys. It's like we're all young again - not a care in the world, and no responsibilities. As kids we'd forget about everything and play ball all day. Who cared if we forgot to eat! We could always get a drink from one of the neighbors' garden hoses, and if nature called, there were plenty of obliging bushes available. Nobody minded, and those who might didn't know about it, I guess.

I'd stay out there 'til dark when that familiar melodic voice would call, "Daaaayne, time to eat!" Ah, if only we could get ring tones with our Moms' voices. Instead, most of us will eventually answer our cell phones and respond, "Yes, Dear, we're nearly done. Yes, I'll be home soon. Yes, Dear, in plenty of time to clean up and put the leaf in the table. Yes, Dear." No wonder we play football!

We'll head home bruised and tired, dirty, and hungry, but totally invigorated. We'll try to hold onto that rejuvenation for another year - until the next Thanksgiving Blue Bowl. Thanksgiving is for giving thanks to God for His many graces: for family, friends, and for our food, of course, but also for all the trimmings, including football.

Savor and enjoy!

◊ 1 TIMOTHY 4:4 *Everything God created is good, and nothing is to be rejected if it is received with thanksgiving.*

A NIGHT WITH THE FLYERS
– HOCKEY FROM THE INSIDE

"**D**ayne, I never know where you're going to pop up next! What are you up to now?" That's a comment I often hear. It's hard to answer sometimes because even I don't know what's around the corner. My friends compare me to Zelig, the character of Woody Allen's 1983 movie. In the film, Leonard Zelig is described as a human chameleon, habitually turning up in bizarre and unexpected places, blending in with the crowd. Interestingly, Zelig is taken from a German word that means blessed, and I am well aware of the fact that I have been blessed with many wonderful experiences. It's not just by chance that I've been in bear dens, have swum with the sharks, or shaken hands with the President. I'm antsy. I put myself in situations that have the potential to be exciting or to teach me something new. Dreaming is fine, but you have to make dreams come true. That's exactly what this hockey fan did.

I wanted to watch the Flyers skate, but it's not enough for me to sit in the stands. I wanted more. Once, during an Eagles game, I infiltrated the playing field at the Vet posing as a photojournalist, but that wasn't possible with the Flyers. I can run. I can ski. I can swim. But put a pair of skates on my feet and I'm in deep trouble. Still, I yearned for a unique Flyers experience - something beyond the ordinary. Then I envisioned myself as a behind-the-scenes reporter, rubbing shoulders with players, coaches and media mavens. Sure, why not! It could happen. I needed the perfect sidekick

- someone who could stir things up. My sidekick for this adventure would be a 5' 11" 260-pound Jewish fellow. I'd ask my old partner in crime, Larry, to come with me. Larry's a West Philly paradox. A sports historian of sorts, he could give you the quarterback ratings or pitching stats of athletes over the last twenty years. He could do the same for any WWE wrestler you might name. "Lefty Larry," we used to call him. As a pitcher he caused many a bench-clearing brawl by intentionally beaning the first batter he faced in every game. That was the kind of player he was. He can be sincere too. A good family man, sincere and charming, he could even sell sand to an Arab! Larry would be the perfect distraction to allow Dayne, the chameleon, to blend in. All I needed was a plan to execute my Flyers fantasy.

So, early in the season, I talked to my old friend, Bob "The Hound" Kelly, one of the nicest guys I have ever met in professional sports. When I laid out my ambition, he rolled his eyes. "Are you kidding," he asked. "You'd stick out like a sore thumb! You'd never get away with it!" "Come on, Bob," I pleaded, "it could be fun." Then he got a boyish glint in his eye, as if he were about to be sent out for another 45-second whirlwind shift to separate an opposing forward from the puck. Suddenly "The Hound" was more than accommodating. Not only did he get me a press pass and a media guide, but he also arranged for a personal tour of the Wachovia Center - the necessary background material if I was to pull off the charade successfully. He seemed as excited about the scheme as I was. "Wow!" I thought, "Bob has my kind of sense of humor." This would be a sly way to play a joke on the press.

In any Dayne Traveler adventure you can expect a glitch or two. It comes with the territory – I can be as clumsy as I am graceful. So it was no surprise to Larry that we hit a snag right from the start. Was this a premonition of what was to come? "Hound" had told us exactly where and when to meet him, but we got lost. When I called his cell phone, he laughed and said, "How can you get lost in a round building?" He went on mockingly, "I know you're pretty good at what you do, Dayne, but I'm not so sure how smart you are." Eventually, The Hound tracked us down and gave us the royal treatment, showing us everything from private locker rooms to the off-limits training areas. Then he took us to the press box where the "other" members of the media were already watching the game.

A boyhood fantasy was realized as we kept bumping into former "Broad Street Bullies." Larry and I had to pinch ourselves to be sure we weren't dreaming.

We were more excited about seeing our boyhood heroes than we were about the game. Our excitement was noticed by the jaded press corps who began to scrutinize us and, all the while, The Hound was rubbing his chin and smiling slyly.

We got to watch some of the game sitting next to The Hound, absorbing his knowledgeable analysis. After watching the Flyers skate to a hard-fought loss, he led us to the coach's post-game conference where I chimed in and got to ask an intelligent question about the night's goaltending. Not to be outdone, Larry, in his typical way, tried to bait the coach with a question about the inconsistent officiating. There would have been a heavy fine if he had answered. "No comment," was all he would say.

The evening would get better and better. We proceeded with the real reporters to the locker room with me in the lead, and who should I literally bump into but star player Peter Forsberg. Our cover was nearly blown during the interviews with the players, when Larry started asking some pretty obnoxious questions. I had wanted him to lay low for a while, but I guess, in the excitement, he couldn't help himself. All the heads in the room began turning toward us. The reporters were really scrutinizing us now. Then I noticed that Larry was using a disposable camera. It was becoming obvious that we were not part of the regular crowd. They must have wondered where we came from, and probably wished we'd go back. One of the Flyers "beat" reporters was checking Larry's press credentials with a "Who the hell is this guy?" look on his face. He looked certain that he would get him expelled, but The Hound's press pass held up to his scrutiny. I thought I'd pee my pants if I started laughing. I had to bite my lip, and all the while, The Hound grinned. We barely managed to escape unexposed.

After the near fiasco in the locker room, as we were getting ready to leave, there was another "Dayne" moment. Who should we run into but one of the hardest working men in Philadelphia sports media, Howard Eskin. I introduced myself, mentioning that I write a news column, and I gave him a copy of my book (which I just happened to have with me). Howard is a controversial radio host with an "in-your-face" style, and he can seem very intimidating, but he also works tirelessly for Philadelphia charities. I asked him if I might interview him, and to my surprise, he didn't just blow me off. He agreed! The Hound muttered softly, "Oh boy, this oughta be good." I was ready for a confrontational interview, but not so! In person, I found Howard Eskin to be gracious and accommodating. He answered all of my questions with knowledge and patience. Unexpectedly, he was quite the gentleman.

Afterward, as we were leaving, I apologized to The Hound for Larry's hilarious, but embarrassing behavior. "Don't worry about it," he said, "those guys needed a little livening up. I had a lot of fun - more than you know." Gracious until the end, Hound walked us to the exit, expressing concern that my expectations hadn't been met.

"Bob," I replied, "the only thing that could top tonight is

if the Flyers capture Lord Stanley's cup this year."

Go Flyers!

◊   PSALM 107:8-9   *...give thanks to the Lord for His unfailing love and His wonderful deeds for men, for He satisfies the thirsty and fills the hungry with good things.*

MOUNTAIN RUSH

Spring had been mild and colorful. Every region has its charms, and northeastern Pennsylvania's Pocono Mountains are certainly no exception to that rule, but I longed to return to my favorite haunts, the beauties of America's Wild West. I visit Wyoming several times each year - the majestic Tetons and Yellowstone National Park feel like my back yard. But just over the eastern border, South Dakota beckoned with its Badlands, its Black Hills, and all the cowboy history that a city kid could hope for. We had been looking forward to this trip out west. As I was going over our itinerary for a book signing, my daughter entered the room with a concerned look on her face.

"What's the matter, Rachael?" I asked.

"Oh, Mister Bateman's given us a hard geology project," she explained.

Scott Bateman is everybody's favorite elementary school teacher at Delaware County Christian School. An excellent educator and always full of fun, he has inspired many youngsters to shine. His lessons are clever and valuable. How could I get my daughter to appreciate her assignment?

"Why would you be concerned?" I probed. "What's he got you doing?"

"We have to collect all these samples of different kinds of rocks and I don't know where to find them."

Images of the Black Hills and Mount Rushmore flooded my mind.

"Have no fear, your daddy, Dayne Traveler, is here," I

replied. "I've already made arrangements with Mr. Bateman to let you take this long weekend for a field trip across the country. It'll be another Rachael and Daddy adventure! (Throughout her childhood, we had taken "Rachael and Daddy adventures" when instruction was necessary for things like hiking, learning to ride her bike, learning to swim, or snorkeling in the Caribbean.) We're going to a place that's a geologist's dream!" I said. "They've got rocks like you've never seen. You'll have the best project in your class! And you'll even learn some history!"

"Wow, that's great, Dad," she said, now enthusiastic.

On a morning in late April our family boarded the flight west. Approaching the airport in Rapid City, SD we could see the Black Hills in the distance, and it was obvious how they had gotten their name. Our destination was an hour's drive north to Deadwood, but going through Sturgis and Boulder Canyon would be a picturesque preview of what was to come - and an appetizer for our lunch at Kevin Costner's place, Diamond Lil's, where Costner displays many of the costumes that were worn in his films. This is also where Costner's film, Dances With Wolves, was made and we would be visiting several sites we had seen in that film. Costner had fallen in love with this place, and for good reason.

Our itinerary had been prepared beforehand and Wes Pederson, the founder of Discovery Tours, turned out to be our greatest asset. Spontaneity has its good points, but there was work to be done on this trip. Wes, a remarkable combination of military veteran, artist and scholar, was born and raised here, and was thoroughly familiar with the region. Wes created an educational experience for us full of fabulous sights and adventures. Cowboy history and folklore saturate this place and I was determined to separate fact from fiction. Glancing over one of our brochures, I remarked, "You know, it wasn't really so long ago that this was a wild and dangerous place. I can almost hear Wild Bill Hickok's spurs jangling in the street." Wes showed us Saloon #10 where, in 1879, Hickok was shot in the back of the head by that coward, Jack McCall.

We walked through the Bullock Hotel, built by Seth Bullock, the first sheriff of Deadwood and a friend of "Rough Rider" Teddy Roosevelt. Roosevelt would later have a great impact on the entire region as president. Just as interesting as Deadwood itself was Mt. Moriah cemetery ("Boot Hill"), where we stood by the graves of Wild Bill, and Calamity Jane, and Potato Creek Johnny. Our first day in South Dakota was capped with dinner at the Deadwood Social Club. It had been a full day. Day two would be more geologic.

We were headed for Keystone, south of Deadwood. Why Keystone?

It's the location of one of the largest geological wonders in the world, Mount Rushmore. Originally, the idea had been to carve a tribute to some local Western hero or another, but when the immigrant sculptor, Gutzon Borglum first saw the grandeur of the site high above the plains in the heartland of America, he knew that it had to be more. This would be a national tribute. The choice of four of our greatest presidents wasn't very difficult - Washington, the father of the nation, Jefferson, the visionary expansionist, Roosevelt, the conservationist and protector of the working man, and Lincoln, the preserver of the union. It was Borglum's way of saying, "This is what it means to be an American."

I had only told my daughter that we were going to look at some big rocks and maybe find some samples to take back to Mr. Bateman, but I intended to surprise her with this great national monument. Along the way we stopped at the largest lake in the Black Hills, Pactola Lake, but Rushmore drew us hypnotically, first framed in the tunnel archways of the Iron Mountain Road, and then viewed from various angles in grand panoramas as we approached. Mount Rushmore is spectacular. Its overwhelming size has always captured men's imaginations, but more, "it awakens the heart and it lightens the face." It made us feel proud to be Americans.

That afternoon we were able to find samples of granite, sandstone, mica, and rose quartz. Mr. Bateman would be pleased. Then it was off to Custer State Park and past the "Cathedral Spires", overlooking the very narrow tunnel called the "Needle's Eye". Visible in the distance were pronghorn antelope, big horn sheep and North American Bison. The bison has definitely made a comeback from the edge of extinction, and the mountain lion sits at the top of the food chain. Sadly, though, there are no bears left in the region. White hunters wiped them out long ago. Before we headed for the Crazy Horse Monument, we hiked around Sylvan Lake to enjoy the refreshing air and vistas. Crazyhorse Monument, the largest sculpture on earth, is a work that's been in progress since 1948. The sculptor has died but his family is keeping their father's dream alive, and hope to complete it in the decades to come. If George Custer can have a state park, Crazy Horse should receive some recognition too. It's only fair. Much of the history of the region is tied up in these two individuals. The Black Hills had always been a special place for the Indians. They revered this land. When gold was discovered, though, there was an influx of greedy treasure hunters who eventually needed military protection. The rest is history. Highway 385 took us back to Deadwood where we reflected on the natural beauties we had seen this day.

Day three began with a visit to the summit of the third highest peak east of the Rockies or west of the Swiss Alps, Terry Peak. On a clear day you can see five states from the summit: North Dakota, South Dakota, Wyoming, Montana and Nebraska. Then Wes led us past Cheyenne Crossing and on to Roughlock Falls, below the Indian camp that was filmed in Dances With Wolves. But we were headed for what would be the highlight of our trip, Spearfish Canyon. This area is beautiful almost beyond description, like a scene right out of a John Wayne movie. The depths and the heights, and the colorful, high, sun-warmed canyon walls aroused our minds to consider God's wonderful creation. We hiked through the canyon, following the stream to the base of Spearfish Falls. I know what you're thinking – shouldn't every adventure have a Dayne Traveler moment? Well, there was a moment, but not a typical one. It was, none the less, memorable. We were all together by the stream admiring Spearfish Falls, but I just had to get closer. I wanted to wade across and get into the mist from the falling water. As I kicked off my shoes and socks, Wes cautioned, "Watch it, Dayne, that water's pretty cold." That's not warning enough to slow me down.

I splashed my way through the stream right up to the falls. Wes was right. By then my legs were numb with cold, but I didn't mind. Standing in the mist with my arms outstretched, I was just happy to be alive. With a tear in my eye, I thanked God for the joy that I felt.

Afterwards we visited Bridal Veil Falls, with its own particular beauty, and in the town of Spearfish we stopped briefly at the historic DC Booth Fish Hatchery before heading west into Wyoming. In Aladdin (population 15), we could see our nation's first national monument, Devil's Tower, in the distance. Here was another geologic memory for Rachael to take back home. I had figured that as long as we were in the vicinity, we couldn't pass it up. (Hats off to Teddy Roosevelt for his vision.) This is the gigantic rock formation that was popularized in Steven Spielberg's 70's movie, Close Encounters of the Third Kind. We were all ready to stretch our legs, so we hiked around the tower and watched several climbers of doubtful judgment, attempting to scale the 867-foot heights. As the day was drawing to a close we turned east again, past a prairie dog town, through Sundance, Wyoming and back past Spearfish to our base camp in Deadwood, South Dakota.

It would be a working evening for me, speaking and signing copies of *The Adventures of Dayne Traveler*. The signing went well but, I must confess, my mind was preoccupied. All the while I was thinking about our current adventure. Our flight out of Rapid City was at 6:00 a.m. the next morning. From the window seat of the plane we waved a fond farewell to the beautiful Black Hills, wondering when we might return.

◊   Isaiah 55:12 *The mountains and hills will burst into song before you, and all the trees of the field will clap their hands.*

RACHAEL, RACHAEL

To celebrate my daughter's 14th birthday she was invited on what has become for me an annual winter visit to Pennsylvania bear country. Each year when I showed her photos of my outings, she'd ask if she could come along with me. "When you're old enough," I'd tell her. This year the bear biologist finally gave his permission. The rugged, mile-long hike through the forest didn't faze her a bit, and the 40-degree descent to the den's entrance beneath a large fallen tree was simply taken in stride. I shouldn't have been surprised, though. She's encountered rough terrain and wild animals before on our travels. For Rachael, it was just a typical outing with Dad. She's had more than her share of unusual experiences, and sometimes I wonder if she has been desensitized to it all. But when the biologist handed a baby bear to Rachael, I basked in the warmth of her smile. I could see that she felt the same sense of wonder and awe that I felt the first time I entered a den and held a cub.

My life has been full but not all of it has been pleasant. Often I'm reminded of my own weaknesses and faults. I've tried to enable Rachael to have adventures but, as I'm prone to live "close to the edge," I sometimes worry about passing on to her my more reckless traits. While I want her to enjoy life to the fullest, I don't want her to experience some of the trials that I've had. I guess the bottom line is that I want to raise her to be a strong, and wise, and sophisticated and moral young lady, but I don't want her to be hurt getting there. In this regard, I'm just your typical daddy. I'm still learning how to play the part. If she were a son instead of a daughter, things might be easier. Her femininity, however, has taught me that there really is a double-standard at work here, but I can't help that. When Rachael was a toddler, I found a photograph that really appealed to me. In it I saw a likeness of my daughter and me. The photo was of a very large wolf, standing guard, straddled over a kitten. His teeth aren't bared, but his expression is very serious, as if he's saying, "Go ahead and try to hurt her – 'Make my day.'" Pointing at the two figures, I told Rachael, "The wolf, that's me. The kitten is you. And as long as I live, I'll be there to protect you." We had the picture framed to hang in her room.

Throughout her life we've shared teaching opportunities that have meant so much to us. I remember so well my father and my grandfather taking me to special places, and the power of those experiences. There's nothing like actual hands on experience. I had decided early on that I wanted the same for my daughter, so she's been able to try all sorts of things; some things that other kids don't get to do until they're adults – maybe never. I want her to be there touching, and tasting and smelling and feeling all the experiences she can, hoping that it might open her eyes and her mind to the vast beauty of the world and the possibilities that await her. I'm tugged between two opposing purposes, though. On the one hand I want to provide her with unique opportunities, but on the other hand, I don't want to spoil her. Sometimes I sit her down to say, "You know, Rachael, not all kids get to do the things that you do. I want you to appreciate that." I am gratified, however, by reports from teachers and friends about her gracious behavior and her tender spirit. I want more for her and, fortunately, I have been able to provide her with some wonderful experiences. I confess that I may have been as extreme in my approach to this as I am in everything else. Even with simple things, it seems that I just can't help myself.

Other kids went to the mall to sit on Santa's lap, but at

our house Santa visited her, and ate her cookies while she played the piano for him. Unexpectedly, she asked where his reindeer were. If I had anticipated that, I might have arranged for some reindeer too. Other children get to go to the zoo, but for Rachael's fourth birthday the petting zoo came to her. Safe within the confines of the back yard we had bobcats, rabbits, goats, snakes, a pony – but when I wanted to lead her on the pony through the gate and down the sidewalk, her mother had to rein me in. "She's only four," she told me. "She doesn't need to experience everything in one birthday!" Sometimes I just can't help myself. If I knew she wanted to be an astronaut, I'd probably start construction of a rocket in the back yard. There are no lengths I won't go to if I'm able. So it is that she's been to exotic beaches and has seen colorful marine life firsthand that others have only seen in pictures. She's biked through mountain forests and tropical jungles. She's skied beside me on mountaintops and has taken in the beautiful vistas. She's attended professional sports events and has seen her favorite athletes up close. She's traveled with the family to world-renowned art museums and national landmarks to see firsthand some of the things she was studying in school. If she's shown interest in something, she's received the best instruction. I can't help it. It's the way I learned about life. It's what I want for her.

My own mother was young when she died, but if she had lived longer she would have suffered a million deaths worrying about my activities. I want to give Rachael a full taste of the Dayne Traveler experience, but always in the back of my mind is the thought that I might be planting some dangerous seeds too. Fearing that I might be her worst influence I've tried to teach her what I know, while downplaying the more extreme activities. I try to steer her toward the sophisticated, rather than the risky. But Rachael has shown such a sense of adventure in all the things she's done that I wondered if

I might have created future heartaches for myself. While I may feel the need to live close to the edge, I don't want to create the same spirit in Rachael. But as much as I have tried to control the situations, for Rachael, the extreme ones seem to have become the norm. It's like a double-edged sword, showing her so much. Sure, I want her to be fearless, but I don't want her to be too much like her dad. At nine years old Rachael asked, "Daddy, who is Dayne Traveler?" Now, at fourteen, she knows him all too well. He may sometimes try to mask it, but she knows he's wild at heart.

Watching Rachael as she nestled the bear cub in her arms, I had to laugh at the ease with which she's taken it all in stride – and it worried me a bit, recognizing Dayne Traveler in the miniature. Aw, who was I kidding? I know well that it's when I've been in extreme situations that I've learned the most – that I've come to know myself best. And that's when I've been drawn closest to the Lord. Could I want less for my Rachael?

◊   PROVERBS 22:6 *Train up a child in the way he should go and when he is old, he shall not depart from it.*

ROCKY MOUNTAIN JOE

L ike the spots on a leopard...
    Each huckster along 9th Street had his goods
impeccably arranged. Links of Italian hot sausage,
balls of mozzarella cheese, and cloves of elephant garlic hung
prominently in store windows. The competing aromas of
pork roast and fresh baked bread filled the air, occasionally
overpowered by the stench of garbage emanating from
a dumpster. Some things never change. If I had been
anywhere but Philadelphia's Italian Market, the revolting
odor might have driven me away, but I could never pass on
an opportunity to take a nostalgic stroll through this old
neighborhood. My brother-in-law, Joe, had wanted to spend
Saturday morning on 9th Street. It provided an opportunity
to discuss the itinerary for our trip to Jackson Hole.

Joe is stereotypically Philadelphia-Italian. This is
distinguishable from the average Italian-American. He looks
tough, talks gruff and plays rough, but beneath his middle-
aged bulge and gold chains lies a warm heart. Walking from
veggie stand to veggie stand, I visualized him roaming the
streets of Jackson like fish out of water. Joe had never been
to Wyoming.

My first taste of the Wild West had prompted me to
dress the part of a cowhand but I wore my Philly heart on my
sleeve. Yep, you can take the boy out of the city but... Well,
you get the point. Fortunately, Jackson's residents were not
offended by my, shall we say, lack of knowledge about the
ways of the West. Instead, they found it endearing. But
watching Joe wheel and deal in the Italian Market, I began

to seriously doubt that this real estate investor extraordinaire and indomitable mortal would be as well received out West.

Either way, I had many excursions lined up for us in Jackson and I was bursting to divulge my plans. Joe, however, rambled a few feet behind me, talking to each storeowner. I wished he would just buy his specialty meats and gargantuan wedge of sharp provolone and be done with it.

I had long been intrigued by the idea of hiking Grand Teton National Park, especially around Jenny Lake. That particular loop is a 22-mile trail that begins on the south side of the lake, circles three miles around it, and then proceeds at a slight incline toward the beautiful Hidden Falls. A steeper incline leads to Inspiration Point which overlooks Jenny Lake. At this point most tourists will turn around, take the ferry back across the lake and call it a day. Some tourists continue to Cascade Canyon. Fewer yet go on to Solitude Lake, a glacier lake about 9400 feet above sea level, just past the halfway mark on the trail. The truly adventurous may make a two-day hike of the entire loop by setting up camp near Solitude Lake. Just beyond the glacier lake is an elevation gain of almost 3000 ft. known as Paint Brush Divide. Making it to the top of the Divide is a commendable feat. The descent from that point, although easier to trek, is a unique challenge because it puts a strain on muscles that are not used frequently, even by the most devoted workout enthusiasts. Holly Lake and String Lake are two welcomed interludes on the trail down from Paint Brush Divide.

As tough as it is, the physicality of the hike is actually the lesser challenge of the adventure. Besides the natural geographic dangers along the trail, there is an abundance of wildlife. The Teton ecosystem includes grizzly bears, black bears, mountain lions, wolves, coyotes, moose, and many more species.

On a recent trip west, I spoke to one of my neighbors

about my desire to do the entire 22-mile hike. Despite being a Wyoming native, Karen had never taken the challenge. She implored me to contact her the next time I visited. I didn't need any prompting. I phoned Karen right after booking my flight west. We were both interested in completing the climb in one day. Most locals raise an eyebrow at such a notion, but Karen is an avid hiker, and always maintains top physical conditioning. So, even though I had never hiked more than ten miles in a day, I figured I could handle the loop. I didn't doubt my ability for a moment. Blind determination is, after all, my modus operandi.

Now, seeing how Joe couldn't keep pace with me in the Italian Market, I realized he was in no shape to take on such a challenge. That was okay, though. For one day he could get along fine without me because there are plenty of saloons in Jackson. That's more Joe's style, anyway. He had never hiked a day in his life.

When I finally got around to discussing the trip with Joe, I rattled off the names of places I wanted to take him. I casually mentioned his visiting Jackson while Karen and I hiked. With a look of consternation, he blurted out, "I'm going on that hike." I was dumbfounded. I had not prepared for this sort of response and my mind scrambled to find a satisfactory explanation to discourage him.

It would be irresponsible for me to allow him to take such a risk. Not only was he out of shape; he wasn't fit for the altitude. Telling him so would make him that much more determined to go, but simply appeasing him would put him in danger. Not to mention the fact that he'd hold Karen and me back. The whole idea of Joe joining us was nuts. It was unfair to all of us. In a feeble attempt to deter him, I began, "Joe, last year, a man in his mid-fifties had a heart attack and needed to be airlifted from the mountainside."

"Must have been a real wuss," Joe replied.

"Joe, this would be a suicide mission for you."

"That's what you think."

He was beginning to anger me. Finally, I stood about a foot in front of him, looked him square in the eyes and said, "Listen, Joe, if you go on that hike, you're going to ruin it for everybody. I don't want to have to carry your butt through the forest, or to have to turn around after a few miles just because you've got a hard head."

"No problem," he said casually. "Youse just better pray that I don't have to carry your butt out of the woods. 'Cause I'll leave ya for the coyotes."

At that point I laughed. I gave him a hearty slap on the back and dubbed him Rocky Mountain Joe. Like Rocky Balboa, the Italian Stallion, my strong-willed brother-in-law had character and lots of brawn. He just hadn't kept it in shape.

There was still time to work on changing Joe's mind, so I consulted my friends out West. They all agreed that the odds were stacked against us. Even my ski instructor, Gage, who moonlights as a tour guide said, "If you make it to Solitude Lake it would be a nice accomplishment. But I doubt you'll make it even that far before you have to call the Jenny Lake rangers for a medivac.

I had phone conversations with Karen trying to come up a scheme to make Joe change his mind, but the conversations only caused her to wonder if she should even go. She said that she'd make her decision after meeting him. Great! The whole reason for another trip west was about to be crushed.

I was reading all sorts of facts and statistics to prepare for a confrontation with Joe, but I figured that embarrassment was the only thing that would change his mind. So I collected ammunition in the form of goads and taunts from some of my friends.

About six weeks after the Italian Market, I saw Joe again, and he actually looked like he'd lost some weight! He confessed that he had begun preparing for the hike, and was taking it seriously. He obviously wasn't about to back down, so rather than trying to embarrass him, I fed his ego to motivate him.

"Joe, I knew you'd step up to the plate," I began. "You're not going to believe some of the comments from nay-sayers." Then, I read this list of remarks:

"Whatever you do, don't fall behind.

"Mountain lions look for the weak and meaty."

"No boozin' the night before, Joe. Got it?"

"Bring oxygen, and don't forget your Bible – for prayer or to smack the coyotes"

"Don't go, Joe – it's a trap!"

"Bring your flask. It's a great pain-killer."

"Take off your skirt and just do it."

"It's not bears you have to outrun – it's at least one other person in your party."

"Joe, repent and get saved before going."

Still somewhat reluctant to take Joe on the hike, I thought that viewing the Tetons from the lake below might humble him. So, on our first day in Jackson, I rented a small motorboat and took him to the base of the mountains. Looking up at the majestic peaks, Joe said, "This is it? No sweat!" He didn't flinch or waver a bit.

We weren't on the lake more than hour when the marina phoned and told us to turn around - a storm was blowing in. Dayne Cousteau here, hurried to start the motor without checking the water's depth. After breaking a propeller, I realized we had drifted into the shallows. I quickly jumped into the lake and pushed the boat into deeper water. With a fifteen-minute return ride ahead of us, we got caught in the perfect storm. As the rain poured heavily upon us, it occurred to me that this little boat incident might be a premonition of what was in store for me on our hike.

In town, I introduced Joe as "Rocky Mountain Joe", the stubborn city boy who thinks he can hike 22 miles in one day." I was trying to get his goat, but it fed his ego even more. Most townspeople laughed, some shook their head at his arrogance, and the harder I pushed my agenda, the firmer he stood his ground.

Day two arrived and I needed to go into town to buy some last minute hiking gear. First stop—the outerwear shop. Whatever I do, I always want to look like the guys in the catalogue. Joe was eager to visit the knife shop and was trying to rush me

"Come on, Dayne, you don't need that stuff."

"Joe, you should be looking for the right clothing, too."

"I didn't travel all the way from Philly to improve my wardrobe."

"Oh really, Rocky? Your worn out cut-offs won't feel so comfy after the first mile or two. The least you should do is get some good hiking boots."

"My $29.99 Sketchers® will do just fine."

By the time I finished my purchases, Joe wasn't the only person happy to see us leave the shop. The sales clerks had had about enough of his loutish commentary, even though it was directed at me.

At the knife shop, I picked up some string, a tarp, and other supplies for an impromptu shelter. There was, after all, a good possibility that we'd have to spend the night on the mountain. Joe was mulling over Rambo-weaponry. "I'm not going into the woods unarmed," he said. "I'm getting a knife." His sentiment was all too familiar, and I wasn't one to argue the point. Joe picked out his knife and we made our way to the cashier. I asked the clerk for a map. Joe asked for flint and steel.

"Joe, I already have 15 boxes of waterproof matches and a lighter."

"I don't care what ya have. I want flint and steel!"

"You've been watching way too many episodes of Survivor.

The clerk interrupted our bickering. "Campfires are banned this year because of the drought," he said.

Inquisitively, I responded, "You mean to tell me that if you were stuck out there in the dark, you wouldn't light a small fire?"

"Absolutely not."

"You'd sit in the dark all night long?"

"Yes," he replied candidly.

"You know what," Joe chimed in, "I'd light three fires. Especially out there with grizzlies runnin' 'round. And if a ranger came along and told me to put them out, I guess I'd have to take him on, too. It's bad enough we can't carry guns. I'm not gonna get stuck in the woods in the middle of the night without a fire."

The clerk was surprised and angered by Joe's brazenness. "Where are you guys from?" He asked.

"Philly," Joe responded proudly.

"Yeah, you know, 'The city that loves you back,'" I added.

The clerk's conviction made me feel a bit sheepish, so I made a deal with myself. I would only use my matches in an extreme emergency. I doubted, however, that Joe was feeling any remorse.

After being embarrassed at each shop we visited, we

headed back to the condo via Snake River. "Hey Dayne, pull over here. Look at all the people swimming! Let's go jump in that crick." No sooner had I parked the car than Joe had his shirt off and was walking into the water with his boots on, as if he was cooling himself off in the Swan Fountain on the Parkway. I followed in bare feet as Joe headed toward the island that separated the swimming area from the river's rapids.

Like Butch Cassidy and the Sundance Kid wanna-be's, both of us had the same harebrained idea—to let the rapids carry us. I entered the rapids first. I knew better than to let my feet down. I might catch my foot on a rock and end up breaking a leg, but holding my feet high meant sacrificing resistance. You'd think I would have learned my lesson about the power of water after a nearly deadly kayaking incident. It was like déjà vu all over again! Luckily, I was able to grab hold of some bushes and make my way up a little embankment to a rock-covered path. The sun was high and the air had warmed to about 90° but on my bare feet, the rocks felt like red-hot coals.

I made it back to the dirt area where we had entered the lake, but Joe was nowhere to be found. I feared that he had tried unsuccessfully to copy me. Then I noticed a few swimmers chuckling and pointing downstream. There was Joe riding a seven-foot log like a rocket in the rapids. A roar of laughter erupted when he teetered and fell off. Joe swam to the embankment and, climbing up, he noticed the small assembly. Like Rocky, racing up the Art Museum steps, he raised his arms in the air and ran toward us. The group dispersed. Some were amused; others shook their heads, appalled by our display of immaturity, asking, "Who are those guys?"

We went home to clean up and prepare for dinner with Karen. It was the night of the big meeting. I didn't dare give

Joe any inkling of the anguish I felt. If he rubbed Karen the wrong way, I'd be stuck hiking 22-miles with Joe as my ball and chain.

We met Karen at a restaurant called the Mangy Moose. As it turned out, the homey tavern was the perfect setting in which to introduce Joe. While we loaded up on carbs in preparation for the next day's big event, Joe enjoyed a steak, medium rare. At the end of the evening, as Joe polished off his third glass of fire water and finished his $20.00 cigar, I pulled Karen aside to say that I would totally understand if she wanted to back out of the hike. To my surprise, Karen found Joe's quirky disposition delightful. "I wouldn't miss this for the world," she replied. "Even if we don't make it, it will be thoroughly entertaining."

On our way home from the restaurant, Joe and I spotted a coyote roaming in an open field. As I often do, I pulled over to observe the beautiful creature in his environment. I know better than to get out of the car and had mistakenly taken for granted that Joe did, too. He jumped out of the car, ignored my warning, and walked toward the coyote whistling at it as if it were a stray dog. The coyote looked up at Joe with a "You gotta be kidding me" sort of look. This prairie wolf had as much attitude as Rocky Mountain Joe did. We got back in the car and I hit the gas, determined to get home without another incident.

We packed our lunches that evening, knowing we would have an early wake up call. My lunch was simple: a half dozen nutrition and power bars, enough fluid for two days, and Jackson M&Ms® (Advil®). Joe packed some power bars along with a couple of sandwiches, which he placed in a plastic bag and tied to his backpack. "You are going to be walking bait for any wild animal," I said. He ignored me.

The next morning I was quietly eating my oatmeal when Joe came out of the guest room. "Ready to go?" I asked cheerfully. "Oh yeah," he replied. "Just git some coffee in my veins and I'll be good to go." Right then it dawned on me that I never saw Joe without his layers of gold chains. He didn't even take them off to sleep. And sure enough, he was wearing the armor on the hike too, with his tee shirt, cut-off jeans, and $29.99 Sketchers®.

The three of us assembled at the South Jenny Lake parking lot at 6:00 AM. Our plan was to have Karen, "The Rabbit", set the pace. Joe and I sensed early on that we would be dead soon if we continued to let her lead. I made Joe take the lead but he was much too slow. Finally, we all concurred: I would lead and we would take frequent breaks.

Our convoy—Dayne Traveler, The Rabbit, and Rocky Mountain Joe—made good time around Jenny Lake. We took in the gorgeous views of Hidden Falls and made our way up to Inspiration Point before we took our first break. It was just a few minutes past 7:00 and we had beaten the first ferry to the other side of the lake. Along the way, we saw lots of berry bushes, which put us on guard for bears.

When we resumed, we made our way toward Cascade Canyon. In terms of beauty, the hike was everything that I expected, and Joe was a source of comic relief the whole time, commenting about all the bets he would collect on when he got back home. As for the level of difficulty, the hike didn't seem all that tough. There were plenty of little streams along the way where we were able to cool off. In fact, by the time we saw the first sign directing us toward Solitude Lake, Joe and I were feeling mighty confident, almost cocky

Before reaching Solitude Lake, we met a park ranger. He looked curiously at Joe whose Rambo knife was displayed prominently across his chest over his gold chains. Sandwiches still dangled from his backpack. When I asked how far we were from Solitude Lake, the befuddled ranger pointed upward and said, "You are less than a couple of miles away. And just over yonder is Paint Brush Divide." Our jaws dropped. I had read about the divide, but never fully understood the magnitude of its incline—a vertical increase of about three thousand feet. Joe and I were immediately humbled. We were, in fact, demoralized.

As soon as we reached Solitude Lake, Joe plunged in head first. I followed. What a relief! After a twenty-minute break, we began to walk switchback style up the divide and for the first time it dawned on us that the nay-sayers might be right. We had to stop every twenty feet or so! Karen and I had been doing pretty well but Joe was struggling. Then fifteen minutes into the climb, Joe "hit the wall." Our breaks had increased to every ten feet. Karen continued to encourage him, congratulating him as he mustered all the fortitude, strength, and effort he had to get up that mountain. I piped in, reminding him about all the money he could collect from bets. I was thankful that prior to the trip I had sought directions on making a makeshift shelter. It had become increasingly obvious that it might take Joe the entire day just to scale the divide. When I mentioned setting up camp, Karen would hear none of it and she encouraged him even harder.

When we thought we were at the top, I spotted two people several hundred feet ahead, even further up the mountain. Joe said I was hallucinating and I hoped he was right. I couldn't imagine that we had so much further to go. Unfortunately, I was not hallucinating, and Joe let out a few profanities when it became clear that there was still a long vertical climb ahead.

We were near exhaustion when I noticed a small stream of water not far from us. It reminded me of Moses in the wilderness. He was about to give up when the Lord spouted water from a rock to refresh and rejuvenate him. The small stream did the same for us.

With our spirits lifted, we made it to the top. Euphoria overcame each of us, and in the rush of emotion Joe began running down the other side of the divide. His second wind was a relief for both Karen and me. We tried to warn Joe to take the downside cautiously, but like a rebellious teen, he did not listen.

As we eased our way down, it dawned on me that we hadn't seen much wildlife. Then, within minutes, I spotted a bull moose on the trail, thirty yards ahead of us. Joe picked up a rock, which alarmed Karen. "That's not the Wyoming way," she said curtly. "It's the Philly way," Joe replied. Thankfully, he relented. The locals are more afraid of being mauled by a moose than by a bear. We waited patiently, and soon the moose went on his merry way.

With four miles or so left on the hike, Joe and I were really feeling the physical effects of the ordeal. We began to lag, and Karen was becoming impatient. She wanted to finish before sundown and insisted on taking the lead to set a faster pace. We willingly gave in.

The adrenaline rush prompted by our close encounter with the moose was just an opening act. About a half-mile from String Lake we rounded a bend and Karen turned abruptly toward me and said, "B-b-b---bear." Joe was twenty-feet behind us. We quickly began to side step away from the bear. I didn't get a good look at the bear but because of its cinnamon coloring, I thought it was a grizzly. I nervously reached for my bear spray. Joe, catching up, pulled out his knife. Two girls from Georgia had caught up with us and gleefully said, "What are ya'll doing." We pointed toward the bear and they said that he was just a black bear eating berries. They told Joe to put his knife away and Karen joined them in their plea, as I did. He was reluctant. One of the young ladies said firmly, "Give me the knife." Joe chuckled eerily, "Are you kiddin' me? I wouldn't give it to you if you were my own mother." The last thing we needed now was an argument to arouse the bear. I had to diffuse the tension. I suggested that we form an alliance and calmly walk right past the creature. Everyone agreed.

The girls from Georgia went first followed by Karen, Joe and me. "Isn't this sort of wimpy of us to make the girls go first," Joe whispered to me. "Yeah," I said nervously, "but right now the fact is that they may be braver. Think about this, though. Once we get past the bear, you and I will be the first in his path if he decides to attack. So actually, we're the valiant ones." I wasn't sure if this made sense but Joe didn't argue the point.

The bear ignored us as he continued chomping on his berries. Once in the clear, we were able to joke and laugh for the last quarter mile of the hike. Joe won the girls' affection. They were savvy and knew that beneath his rough and rugged "Hey yo!" façade there was a cuddly teddy bear.

As our adventure wound down, I apologized for holding Karen back. She reassured me, however, that although she might have made better time on her own, she was impressed and inspired by our display of determination, zeal, and love for life.

When we were literally out of the woods, Joe threw both arms in the air. He hadn't scaled the Art Museum steps but he exemplified something much more: good old Philly grit.

◊ EXODUS 17:5-6 ...*The Lord said to Moses, "Walk on ahead of the people. Take with you some of the elders of Israel, and take in your hand the staff with which you struck the Nile, and go. I will stand there before you by the rock at Horeb. Strike the rock, and water will come out of it for the people to drink."*

NORTH TO ALASKA

I was walking from the first viewing platform through the woods to the second one by the falls. It was a beautiful day! The sun was bright, the air was cool and crisp, and the silence of the woods had me feeling relaxed, thinking of heaven and softly humming Amazing Grace as I stepped over rocks and roots. It had been picture perfect – until now. Suddenly the forest itself seemed to shift right in front of me, and a rush of adrenaline stopped me in my tracks. Just ten steps ahead, a thousand-pound Alaskan grizzly bear had silently appeared. It seemed as big as a truck! I'd watched them on National Geographic and on Discovery Channel, but unexpectedly standing right in front of one I just didn't know how to respond. When you actually see an animal that enormous, so close, you try not to panic! I did a rapid about face, gazed over my shoulder, locked eyes with the behemoth and moved quickly back up the trail. Suddenly I realized that the bear might interpret my hasty movement as panic, and see me as prey. The shock of the encounter had made me stupidly forget the orientation the Rangers' had given upon my arrival, and everything I had ever learned about bears. There was real danger here.

"You've done it this time, Dayne," I thought to myself. "This is not good. Is this really what you were looking for? Sure, you like the sensation and the intensity of close encounters, but this close? Wow! If this bear wants you, you're his!"

A psychologist might say that my tendency to wander off the beaten path is driven by a subconscious need to take risk. He might say it's a reckless attempt to get a thrill by cheating death. I don't disagree, but in this case it was much simpler than that. I just hadn't expected to get this close so suddenly! Fortunately, the LORD was watching over me, and the bear was more interested in where it was going than in my presence. It crossed the path and quietly disappeared into the Alaskan wilderness. My close encounter had been about forty yards closer than permitted, and it definitely had my heart pounding! If I was going to survive the coming week I would have to be more vigilant.

Remote and wild places have been my passion ever since my first excursion into northern Minnesota in the Outward Bound program. That experience changed the direction of my life and led me on a winding path that I knew would eventually lead me to Alaska. Everything else had just been a practice run. Now Alaska would give me a chance to satisfy my favorite longings – being out in the wild, fly fishing, and finally getting to see these great brown bears. Doing all three in one great adventure was hard to pass up. That's why I finally came here to one of the most isolated places in North America. This was the real deal!

Alaska is WILD! It seems like everyone and everything has an attitude – the weather, the geology, the bears, the moose, the rivers and streams, the guides and the travelers, the fishermen and the fish, even the insects – they're all "in your face." The Alaskan Peninsula is about the most unpredictable place I've ever seen. Everywhere you look, it's wild and hazardous and there's tension everywhere! My unexpected run-in with Alaska's prime predator had me reconsidering just how dangerous this adventure could be.

I had arranged to stay for a week here at Brooks lodge in Alaska's remote Katmai National Park. Brooks Lodge ain't no Hilton. It's more like a boot camp in the woods. The lodge's owner is Sonny Peterson. Half a century ago, his dad, Ray, established a fishing lodge here in the middle of this National Park, where Naknek Lake and Brooks Lake nearly touch. Visitors come here from all over the world for some of the best fly fishing to be found. It's world-class fly fishing for sure, but it's the proximity of the human and bear populations that's become the main attraction! The principle rule is that you keep at least fifty yards away from any bear. That's more difficult than it sounds.

I intended to do some hiking the following day, but was still a little shaken after my recent close encounter. I steeled my nerves, though, and started out the next day with a group of others. When we arrived at the first viewing platform, however, the bears were so numerous that there was a traffic jam of hikers and photographers, all waiting to continue their treks. The fifty yard rule was well in place, so there was little to do but wait for the bears to move along. I wanted to make better use of my time, so I returned to camp and rented a kayak to detour around the traffic jam and explore Nanek Lake. I was informed that the "five-minute rules" were in effect – If I didn't show up within five minutes of my expected return time, Search and Rescue would be coming to get me, and if I fell into the frigid water I'd have about five minutes to live! What a wake up call! With these warnings in mind I started out. While everybody else bided their time at the falls, I'd be enjoying scenery that few people will ever get to see.

My paddle made a calming sort of swooshing sound with each dip. In the quiet along lake's shore it was the only sound to be heard for miles. The steady breeze that kept the insects away was moving picturesque clouds slowly across the autumn sky. Gliding through the cold water at a relaxed pace, I spotted several bears farther down the shoreline. Off in the distance, a moose was in the water near the grassy shore, and to my left was a postcard view of snowcapped mountains. I thought, "Yeah, I could get used to this."

To my right was the famous Valley of Ten Thousand Smokes, named by botanist, Dr. Robert Griggs in 1916 when he explored the area after the 1912 volcanic eruption that devastated the region. The Alaskan peninsula is one of the most seismically active regions on earth. Novarupta (literally New Eruption) was the largest volcanic eruption of the 20th century, releasing six cubic miles of ash, and covering more than 40 sq. miles of a nearby mountain valley to depths of up to 700 feet. The entire native population had to be evacuated, and relocated. Novarupta was ten times greater than Mount. St. Helen's eruption in 1980, making St. Helen's seem like a sneeze in comparison. For me, this was just one more example, one more facet, of Alaska's wildness.

As I was thinking about these things, my attention had strayed from the job at hand – keeping the kayak parallel to the shoreline. I had gotten just a bit too close to the shore and to a very large bear, breaching its comfort zone by about thirty yards. He awakened me from my daydream by suddenly plunging into the water toward my kayak. Doing my best impression of a collegiate rower on the Schuylkill River, I hastily retreated into deeper water where the bear couldn't reach. Wow, that was close!

"Did you see that," I called incredulously to a more distant boater.

"Yeah," he called back, "you were getting a little too close. He was just letting you know about it! Stay awake, partner. I'm not jumping in to save you!"

It was unnerving! Two strikes against me in two days. Was I going to be the first fatality in fifty years? I needed to make sure I wasn't! I really, really had to stay more vigilant. This wasn't the Poconos. This was the Alaskan peninsula. I paddled back to the camp somewhat shaken, reassessing my personal safety and the practical wisdom of the Park's rules.

I had arranged to go fly fishing the next few days with Tony, an experienced fisherman and guide. With a toothpick in his mouth and his head slightly cocked, you couldn't quite tell if he was smiling at you or sizing you up. What a character! As a Marine, he had volunteered to go to Afghanistan so he could kill the Taliban. A civilian now, I suppose that Alaska was the only place that was still wild enough for him. You might say that Tony was a little eccentric, but look who's talking! We both figured that we'd get along well together.

Toothpick Tony was very knowledgeable about fishing, and he had a few favorite spots to show me. Over the next few days our daily routine was to take a picturesque Jeep ride to the mouth of the river and share the space with the bears. Day one was spent casting for salmon, where Tony educated me about their importance.

Throughout their life cycle, the salmon are food for so many other species; for bald eagles, bears, other fish and the various creatures that forage along the streams. They have been an important food source for the native residents for thousands of years too, and salmon still anchors the local economies.

I could not believe the fight these resilient fish put up! There was no need for fisherman's luck, though. Our fishing was productive. I caught and released dozens of salmon, but my catch of the day was a 9-pound, 29 ½ inch sock-eye salmon.

The next two days we fished for rainbow trout, standing waist-high in the middle of Brooks River casting. Bears were constantly popping in and out of the woods, sometimes swimming within ten yards of us. At one point we were totally surrounded, with no place to retreat. Tony remained as cool as ice and instructed me to remain still. I obeyed, except for the warm liquid dripping down my leg inside my waders. Thankfully, the bears were more interested in gorging on the sock-eye than us. We had good intentions to observe the fifty-yard rule, but try explaining that to the numerous 800-plus pound grizzlies. I can now say that I've actually fished with the grizzly bears in wild Alaska!

As our boat took us back to camp, I thanked Tony for the greatest three days of fly fishing I had ever experienced. Tony could not help but to remark, "You looked a little scared back there when we were surrounded, Dayne." I replied, "Who, me? I knew I could out swim ya!"

As the day of departure neared, I stood outside my room, gazing at the bears in the river. I thought about how I had come full-circle in my love affair with bears, and wondered whether I was guilty of pressing my luck. After all, you don't have to travel all this distance to fish, and you can see bears at the Philadelphia Zoo. But apparently, for all of us here at Brooks Lodge, that just wasn't enough. What was it we were trying to achieve, coming all the way to Alaska? I think it was simply an insatiable desire to get closer than any other experience could provide.

As I pondered all this, a beautiful large bear approached from the woods. A Japanese visitor quickly handed me his camera and motioned that he wanted me to take his picture – with the bear! He rushed straight toward the animal, and then turning his back to it so it could be seen over his shoulder, he motioned, "Take it, take it," beaming a smile for the camera. I couldn't believe it! The bears can be hypnotic, but this was outrageous! Today, however, this gentleman's luck held out, and I won't condemn him. If I hadn't already packed my camera away, who knows what I might have done. And I sure wish I had a shot like that in my scrapbook!

◊   GENESIS 1:1, 31 *In the beginning, God created the heavens and the earth...God saw all that he had made, and it was very good.*

MUSHING

I am continually telling others about the beauties of the western landscapes, and friends have joined me there to see for themselves, but there is one area of true wilderness that I hadn't explored yet. And it's big! The Bridger-Teton National Forest contains nearly three and a half million acres of unspoiled forest, streams, mountains and valleys that have been permanently set aside as a primitive area. The Bridger Forest alone is more than one and three-quarter million acres. But camping there is not for everyone – When you camp in this forest, you're really "roughing it." As they advise visitors, it is "primitive!" But I didn't come here to camp. I had a more interesting way to see the forests.

It was winter, and the snow was abundant. What better way to see this area than by dogsled; by "mushing." In this age of snowmobiles you might think that nobody uses dogsleds anymore, but you'd be wrong. Trappers say that dogs are safer and more dependable in extreme weather conditions. In remote areas dogsleds are used for travel, hauling firewood and equipment and even for mail delivery. Of course, there is the sport aspect of dogsleds too. Everybody's heard of Alaska's 1049 mile Iditarod race, but in the lower forty-eight, Jackson, Wyoming is the starting point for an international race to Park City, Utah. It offers a $100,000 prize and attracts world-class competitors.

I made arrangements through a former Grand Canyon guide and seasoned musher, Stephan, for a dogsled excursion into the Bridger Forest: our destination, Granite Hot Springs, about twenty miles round trip. The kennel was at the head of a trail into Bridger, ten miles from the hot springs. In warmer months, you might drive to the springs and back by car in about half an hour. By dogsled in the winter, though, the outing is an all-day affair. As Stephan took me out to meet the dogs he explained some of the fundamentals of mushing.

"The dogs live outside year-round," he said. "They're conditioned to the cold and they love it. They're smart, have a lot of common sense, and they can find trails in bad conditions. But most of all, they just love to run. It's like a game to them. The sled is a pretty simple affair," he explained. "It's strong enough to carry equipment or a passenger, but it's still light enough for the dogs to pull. The dogs are usually harnessed in pairs, connected to the sled's long gang-line by their tug-lines. The 'lead' dogs are out in front, finding the trail. Behind them, the 'swing' dogs steer the dogs behind them into the trail's curves and turns. The dogs closest to the sled are called 'wheel' dogs. They need to be the calmest dogs in the team so they won't be startled by the sled moving right behind them. The musher stands behind the sled on the runners where he can see and command all the dogs. I run teams of six or eight dogs," he said. "Today I'll run one team of six dogs and one of eight."

"What's the most important thing?" I asked. "What do I need to know to do this?" I needed to know because we had agreed that I'd get to try my hand at mushing solo.

"Since you ski, Dayne, you know about watching your speed and leaning on curves," he answered, "You understand how a high center of gravity can cause you to roll over. You'll pick up the basics on the way to the springs, but in this sport the cardinal rule is 'Never let go of your sled.' If you're out there in the frozen wild and you lose your sled and dogs, it could be the end of your trail."

As we approached the dog sheds on the snow, eighty

dogs began barking and leaping, working themselves into a frenzy. Our arrival meant that it was time for some fun. They all wanted to go out. They'd been trained to run. They were fine dogs, lean and heavily furred, mostly Huskies, but one large wolf-like dog suddenly caught my eye. She was big and beautiful and my mind flashed back to a time when I was a kid.

I had been begging my dad for a dog for a long time, so one Christmas Eve he took me to the pet store in our local mall to look at three German shepherd puppies.

"Which one do you like?" he asked

It was an easy choice. One of them was all full of spunk, overpowering her siblings in the pen – tough but playful.

"That's the one, Dad," I told him. "I want the one with the floppy ear."

I named her Heidi. Our little ten-pound girl eventually grew to an untypical one hundred and ten pound wonder. She was big and spunky and lots of fun. Her floppy ear straightened out, but she never lost her love of play. I taught her to jump over the trash cans, and to fetch a ball. At obedience school, she passed with a 91. I felt she could have done better, but she had a will of her own. Oh, she'd obey, all right, but sometimes she seemed to be pushing the obedience envelope. (They say that dogs resemble their owners.) She loved to roughhouse with the neighbors' dogs, but no other dog could best her. I guess you could say she was the Alpha-female of the neighborhood. She was playful, loveable and affectionate. She never bit or threatened anybody, but I still got a kick out of seeing fear in the eyes of people who didn't know her when we walked down the street. I really loved Heidi. She was a part of the family, and my dad loved her as much as I did.

I had Heidi for ten years, but one day I found the back

gate open and she was gone. Maybe she ran away. Maybe she got out and was stolen. I don't know. I never saw her again. My heart was broken, and I had to swear off having pets. It was terrible not to know her fate and, even now, years later, it's still painful to think about.

Now, there before me in the Wyoming snow was Heidi. Well, it sure seemed like Heidi, big and beautiful and playful. When I dropped to my knees and called her, she came right into my arms, nearly knocking me over with affection and wanting to play. I had forgotten how much I loved dogs.

"Looks like you two should get along OK," Stephan said, laughing. She's your lead dog."

"This adventure's going to be great," I thought to myself.

Stephan was taking two sleds out that morning. It was supposed to be a small, intimate group, but I wondered about that. Stephan and I were to ride the lead sled with six dogs. On the other sled was the "odd couple," Margie and Kevin, said to be travelers and adventurers. I couldn't begin to guess which would be in charge. Margie seemed more of an alpha male than Kevin.

The morning was cold and cloudy and, as Stephan was harnessing the dogs, it started to snow. The dogs loved it. They couldn't wait to run. When the two teams were hitched, off we mushed through the silent forests of Bridger, the only sound the constant shushing of the runners on the snow. The trail was easily visible as we moved through the forest, past rushing streams, distant waterfalls and snowy mountain vistas. The ancient trees were stunning. The air was crisp. Everybody was in high spirits. It was starting to look like the perfect adventure.

Ten exhilarating miles later, we approached the hot springs. I had heard about this place before, but I was surprised by what I saw just the same. The site is open year round. In warmer months it's possible to hike or drive to the springs, but in the winter it's only accessible by skis, snow mobile and, oh yes, by dogsled. Under the government's work projects in the 1930's, a concrete swimming pool had been built here, fed by the hot spring. It is surrounded by a wooden deck, with changing rooms along side. After changing into swim suits, it was a short, barefooted scamper over the snow from the changing rooms to the hot pool. This is the only place I know of where you can relax in 112 degree water while you catch snowflakes on your tongue! While Margie, Kevin and I soaked in the hot water swapping information on our favorite destinations, Stephan cooked a lunch of smoked trout, tea and hot cider over an open fire.

Lunch seemed extra tasty out in nature, as it always does.

When I made the arrangements for this outing, I had hoped I might get to drive a sled solo – I just couldn't pass up such an opportunity. Stephen graciously planned to accommodate me on the return trip. But when he told the others that he, Kevin and Margie would all be in the lead sled, there was a problem. Margie seemed to resent that I would get a sled all to myself. It was explained that the arrangements had been made beforehand, and that's how it was going to be. Stephan and Kevin would ride on the runners and Margie would be the baggage. Off they went. All I had to do was follow. I was in my glory, free to enjoy the scenery along the way, bringing up the rear with my own dog team.

I let the others get a bit ahead. Margie was barking about being treated as cargo, and the sound of bickering spouses was disturbing the peace of forest. After a while I noticed that up ahead Stephan had a problem – he was turning too sharply, and Kevin was leaning the wrong way. His left runner lifted and hovered for a moment a foot off the snow before the sled rolled over completely, mushers, baggage and all.

"So much for the perfect adventure," I laughed, but then suddenly I realized that I was exactly on Stephan' line, moving at the same speed. My runner also started to lift. I could see myself duplicating his roll-out, and getting thrown. I was inexperienced at this and all of my options looked bad, causing the adrenaline to flow. Instinctively, I bailed out – bad move! My sled didn't roll over, but I watched in disbelief as my dogs and sled continued down the trail, straight toward the others. I watched as Stephan gallantly blocked the trail, raising arms trying to bring my team to a stop, and then grasping at the harnesses, but his heroism didn't work. The dogs veered off and the sled crashed into his leg as it passed. Stephan suffered a broken ankle.

Eventually we pulled the scene together – sleds, dogs and mushers. Now our roles had to be changed. Stephan instructed Kevin and Margie to drive one sled, while Stephen, bandaged and in severe pain, would be my passenger in the lead sled, coaching me as I drove the dogs home.

"All right," Kevin told Margie, let's get going. We've got an injured man here." And off we mushed again.

"What do I do if you pass out," I asked, seriously concerned. "Who's going to coach me then?"

"It's OK, Dayne," he replied. "The dogs know the way home. Just keep them running." Stephan managed to remain conscious, and eventually we arrived safely at the kennel. I felt like Sergeant Preston of the Northwest Mounties, leading the way back home.

"Well, Dayne," Stephan said, "you got a little more than you bargained for today, eh? But I thought I told you never to let go of your sled!"

I felt terrible about his injury, and sheepishly apologized, making my best excuses for my inexperience.

I tried to explain the "Dayne Traveler Syndrome" whereby things only go wrong when you're sure they won't. Stephan laughed and forgave my natural reaction to the dangerous and unpredictable situation. He was taking it all in stride.

"Don't worry," he assured me, "I'll be fine." What a guy!

Overall, it was still a great outing. I met interesting people, I learned something new, and I'd swear, I think I found my missing dog. This one's for you, Heidi!

◊   Isaiah 44:23 *Burst into song, you mountains, you forest and all your trees for the Lord has redeemed Jacob. He displays his glory in Israel.*

HEAVEN ON EARTH

O n a rainy Saturday morning when I might normally have been out biking, I sat at my computer exploring "Google Earth." Like an alien visitor I hovered over the planet, then zoomed in to the North American continent, wondering if I could actually locate my little heaven on earth. I had to use the large geographic signposts that I knew to zero in on my objective. Sure, I could just type in my destination, but that would be cheating. Besides, when you're trying to find heaven, you can't just hit "enter." You've got to go through a few twists and turns to reach the gate.

"Let's see," I thought to myself, "where are we? OK, there are the Great Lakes. Scroll, scroll, scroll. Zoom, zoom, zoom. Which is which? There, the big one on the left, that's Superior. And that one is Lake Michigan. OK, scroll, scroll down to the tip. That's Chicago. Turn due west. Click, click, click, across the Mississippi. Click, click, click, and that's the Missouri. Halfway. OK, click, click, click, click, click, click. In the Rockies now, click, click, oooops! That's Great Salt Lake. I'm in Utah. Too far. Back up a little, and now Due North. Up, up, up, up. I've gotta be close now. Maybe zoom in a little closer. Look for lakes. Yeah, that's it, look for lakes. There, there! The one that looks like a big lobster, that's Yellowstone Lake. A little below that and we're almost home."

It was easier finding it on Google Earth than in real life. It took half of my life to actually find the place, and another quarter of it to understand that this was the place my heart longed for.

Teton National Park and Jackson Hole are just south of Yellowstone. They're both in the northwest corner of Wyoming in the most geologically active spot on earth. The entire area lies in the hollow of a gigantic volcanic explosion that happened in ages past, the scale of which we can only imagine. It makes Mt. St. Helen's eruption seem like a hiccup; Krakatoa a mere loud bang. Yellowstone's underground activity is flamboyant, with its geysers, bubbling pools and mudpots. The Tetons, though, are more subtle. The twelve mountains in the Teton range were formed much more recently than their parents, the Rockies. They mark the Teton Fault, a fault line where two great blocks of rock oppose each other. On the east side, what we call Jackson Hole slides beneath the western face of rock, and the Tetons on the west side rise abruptly and majestically above the plain.

I have Thomas Jefferson to thank for all this. His unlikely real estate speculation with the French at the turn of the 19th century gave us the Louisiana Purchase. And then Lewis and Clark were sent to find out just what he had bought. What a shrewd deal it turned out to be! But we haven't always been the best stewards. A century later, we needed Theodore Roosevelt, with the heart of a conservationist, to protect these wild lands. God bless Teddy Roosevelt, and let's not forget the Rockefeller family for their generous contributions.

There's not actually a hole at Jackson Hole. That's just what the old-timers used to call a valley that's surrounded by mountains. Jackson Hole, one of the largest of such valleys in the Rockies, was named after David E. Jackson who trapped in the Snake River country in the early 1800's. He loved this area, and I understand why. Grand Teton National Park is one of the few remaining, nearly intact, temperate zone ecosystems left on the planet. In its 333,000 acres you can find sixty-one species of mammals, more than 300 species of birds, and a thousand species of vascular plants, all thriving as God intended. There are four major habitats here: the alpine zone, coniferous forests, sagebrush flats, and wetlands. There are pristine lakes, streams and waterfalls, vast colorful plains, and heights, and depths and spectacular views everywhere you look. A person could spend a lifetime exploring and enjoying it all. As my friend, Doctor Cloyd has said, "It's a visual smorgasbord."

I've been to Jackson Hole many times in the last decade and have even bought a little place to stay while I'm there. No matter what season I go, there's always some new wonder that amazes me. You've got more chance of seeing wildlife here than any other place I can name. What's your favorite? Eagles, ospreys or hawks? Beavers, bears or bison? Bison, you say? How about herds of bison flowing over the hills like water! How about meeting a grizzly on the path as you hike, or a mountain lion – you ready for that? You prefer elk, you say? Yeah, we've got elk too – no problem! Heck, I've even been chased by a moose! In the summer I've tried my hand at fly-fishing and have caught native cut-throat trout in its clear running streams. I've dived into its glacier lakes and soared like a red-tailed hawk, para-gliding over flower-carpeted meadows. I've ridden horseback in the fall through aspen groves, shaking their clear yellow leaves in the breeze, and have floated silently over the colorful landscape in a hot air balloon. I learned to ski in its mountains, and in the winter I've snow-mobiled and dog-sledded on snowy treks. I've hiked many miles photographing its diverse landscapes and wildlife. I've enjoyed sunrises and sunsets each one different from the last. If I've learned anything about the place it's this – each surprising spectacle surpasses the one before. Just when you think there couldn't possibly be a new thing to see, ten new ones spring up to dazzle the senses. The more I see, the more I come to believe that I've just skimmed the surface. This must be a glimmer of what heaven will be like. But while I'm on earth, Jackson Hole and Grand Teton National Park will do just fine, thank you.

In moments of solitude I gaze in wonder at the landscape but, as magnificent as it is and as abundant the wildlife, it saddens me to realize that this is all just a shadow of its former glory. I try to imagine the wonder that the first explorers experienced coming to the area. There were no roads then, no jets leaving trails across the sky. The rivers were teeming with fish and fur then. The wildlife population was many times greater than what you find now. Occasionally you might have spotted Native Americans living in harmony with nature.

You're truly blessed if you find a location where you're happy and I'm happiest when I'm here. I love this area with a passion. The first time I came here, a love affair began, and it's been an affair that I've been able to share with family and friends. The gracious residents of Jackson share a sense of appreciation of their area with its many beauties. They are protective of it. It's one of the few truly wild places left on earth, and nobody who visits comes away the same. Nowhere else do I feel this sense of marvel at God's creative genius. The people of Jackson understand this, and I'm grateful that they've made this Philly boy feel as welcomed and as loved as an adopted son. Jackson Hole has become my home away from home. When I'm leaving, I'm already looking forward to coming back. It's my little heaven on earth.

◊ GENESIS 1:31 *God saw all that he had made, and it was very good....Thus the heavens and earth were completed in all their vast array.*

THANKFUL

The swollen lymph gland had been removed from my elbow and sent out for biopsy. The results had come back positive. Non-Hotchkins lymphoma had returned.

"Where do we go from here?" I asked Dr. Roush. He was with me through the previous radiation treatments and checkups and he understood how defeated I was feeling. What he now suggested was eventually echoed by two other institutions, Fox Chase and the University of Pennsylvania. Everyone agreed – do nothing. Unless my situation got worse, do nothing. But the fact was that it was possible for my condition to get much more serious than I could even imagine. Although some people go on to lead normal lives, it truly could finish me. The gravity shook me to the core, and I had mixed feelings about their non-course of action. It went against my proactive tendencies – taking challenges head on, and working through difficulties. It seemed like a big chance to take. What should my attitude be? How would I live each day, knowing that the cancer could reoccur, despite my best efforts to stay healthy? How was I to deal with the possibility of death at such a young age? Even as I write this, there's not a day that goes by that I don't think about it. Dealing with the physical aspects – the regular check-ups, the constant examination of my body for lumps – was bad enough, but that wasn't my biggest concern. I needed the comfort of friends and family, and they couldn't have been more supportive, but even more, I needed a sense of peace in the spiritual realm.

At some time in life everyone wonders, "Why am I

here? How did I get here and where am I going when it's all over?" After reflecting on my life, I felt like King Solomon. When he examined his own life he realized that all of his experiences and all of his accomplishments really counted for nothing in the end.

> ◊   ECCLESIASTES 2:10-11 *"I denied myself nothing my eyes desired; I refused my heart no pleasure. My heart took delight in all my work, and this was the reward for all my labor. Yet, when I surveyed all that my hands had done and what I had toiled to achieve, everything was meaningless, a chasing after the wind."*

Just like the great king, as much as I had achieved, I couldn't take it with me. Mortality had the final word. The excitement of life was like chewing gum – the flavor was only for a moment and there was no lasting satisfaction to be found. Nobody knows when their time is up, and no earthly adventure can ever bring true contentment. I've always believed that you work hard to earn the right to play hard. I enjoy the things I do, and I encourage others to enjoy life too, but it all has to be kept in perspective. As enjoyable as my adventures have been, they provide nothing lasting to hold onto. That's not where my comfort is to be found. Even the photographs will fade. Ultimately, it is only my relationship with the Lord that I can depend on. My thoughts kept returning to an adventure that nobody has read about yet – a promise that I had held onto for years.

The movie Citizen Kane tells the story a man who had accumulated money, and art, and power and fame during his life, but the last word he spoke before he died was "rosebud." After being shown the long journey of his life, the viewer finally learns what "rosebud" means – it was the name he had given his sled when he was a little boy. All the wealth and power counted for nothing. He longed for the innocence of his childhood, but he died an unhappy man. My life would not be as futile. My final word wouldn't be "rosebud." For me, it would be "cookies and juice."

I was just ten years old when a Christian family interrupted our baseball game to invite me and my friends to come to a kids' summer Bible school they were holding in their home. I went and it was fun – free cookies and juice, too! Unexpectedly, I emerged a different person. Somewhere during the fun and games, the Gospel had been presented: "There was this great chasm between me and God because of sin," I was informed. "My relationship with God was broken and there was nothing I could do about it. It took a loving God to fix the problem by sending his own Son to earth to pay the penalty for man's sin. It couldn't be done by any of my future achievements. I could never do enough work to pay off the debt. It was settled only by this act of a loving Lord. It was by His grace. It was a gift – just like the cookies and juice." God loved the world so much that he gave His only son, so that anybody who believed in him wouldn't die, but would have eternal life – John 3:16 The teacher asked if anybody wanted to receive Jesus in his heart – Did anyone believe the good news about Jesus? Something clicked in my mind. I understood it. I wanted a restored relationship with God. Up went my hand and my life has never been the same. Of all the things I've done, that was the greatest decision I've ever made. Despite all of my shortcomings, Christ saved "a wretch like me," and I am thankful. I know Jesus as Savior and I want everyone to know the gratitude that I feel. I offer you, the reader, the same proposition. Truly, it will be the greatest decision you ever make.

I'm sure that *The Adventures of Dayne Traveler* will be passed on to family members, friends and acquaintances, and to many whom I'll never meet. It will even be a legacy to my great grandchildren. Will there be a third volume of Dayne Traveler? God willing! But just as I don't know how much time I have left, neither do you. Have your own adventures and enjoy your life to the fullest. Appreciate life's splendors. Observe wildlife whenever you can. Stand under a waterfall with outstretched arms. Stroll down the beach hand in hand with a loved one. Listen to the birds singing their beautiful songs in the morning. Enjoy a sunset. Cherish your loved ones. Kiss and hug your children and tell them how proud you are of them. Forgive offences. Love life and have no regrets. But understand that a life without Jesus – the Lord of Lords, the King of Kings, the Alpha and Omega – none of it matters.

◊   PSALM 27:4 *One thing I ask of the Lord, this is what I seek: that I may dwell in the house of the Lord all the days of my life to gaze upon the beauty of the Lord and to seek him in his temple.*

"I did not tell half of what I saw, for I knew I would not be believed."

— Marco Polo
On his deathbed
1324 A.D.

ACKNOWLEDGMENTS

We believe the Lord Jesus Christ has had his hands on this entire project from its inception. We thank Him for His grace and continue to pray for His guidance.

We sincerely appreciate the endless support and encouragement of family and friends. We are also grateful to each of our team members for their outstanding contributions to *The Adventures of Dayne Traveler – Reflections, Volume 2*:

— Writer and Editor   ***David Gray***

— Writer's Contribution   ***Lorraine Ranalli***
                              Special thanks for Rocky Mountain Joe

— Book/ Cover Designer   ***Avril Losacco,***
                                                        Art Director
                                              LosaccoCreative.com

— Chapter Artwork   ***Abigail Gray,***
                                                   Freelance Artist

— Front & Back Cover Photos   ***Richard Wagner,***
                                            Freelance Photographer

— Treasure Chest logo   ***Elizabeth Lincoln,***
                                                  Artist/ Designer